SCIENCE INTERACTIONS

Course 1

GLENCOE
McGraw-Hill

New York, New York   Columbus, Ohio   Woodland Hills, California   Peoria, Illinois

A Glencoe Program

Science Interactions

Student Edition

Teacher Wraparound Edition

Science Discovery Activities: SE and TE

Teacher Classroom Resources

Laboratory Manual: SE and TAE

Study Guide: SE and TE

Transparency Package

Section Focus Transparencies

Teaching Transparencies

Computer Test Bank

Performance Assessment

Performance Assessment in the Science Classroom

Spanish Resources

Science and Technology Videodisc Series and Teacher Guide

Integrated Science Videodisc Program

MindJogger Videoquizzes

Glencoe/McGraw-Hill

A Division of The McGraw-Hill Companies

Send all inquiries to:
Glencoe/McGraw-Hill
936 Eastwind Drive
Westerville, OH 43081

ISBN 0-02-828060-1

Printed in the United States of America.

2 3 4 5 6 7 8 9 10 11 12 13 14 15 045 05 04 03 02 01 00 99

TABLE OF CONTENTS

* Indicates Design Your Own Investigation

TO THE TEACHER

The Activity Masters in this booklet are expanded versions of Investigate! and Design Your Own Investigation activities featured in each student edition chapter of *Science Interactions: Course 1.* All materials lists, procedures, and questions are repeated so that students will be able to read and complete an activity in most cases without having to have a textbook on the desk or lab table. Activities that require recorded data also have enlarged versions of the Data and Observations table for that activity. All activity Analyzing questions and Concluding and Applying questions are reprinted with rules on which students can write their answers. In addition, for the safety of students, all appropriate safety symbols and caution statements have been reproduced on these expanded pages.

Safety Symbols

These safety symbols are used to indicate possible hazards in the activities. Each activity has appropriate hazard indicators.

	DISPOSAL ALERT This symbol appears when care must be taken to dispose of materials properly.		**ANIMAL SAFETY** This symbol appears whenever live animals are studied and the safety of the animals and the students must be ensured.
	BIOLOGICAL HAZARD This symbol appears when there is danger involving bacteria, fungi, or protists.		**RADIOACTIVE SAFETY** This symbol appears when radioactive materials are used.
	OPEN FLAME ALERT This symbol appears when use of an open flame could cause a fire or an explosion.		**CLOTHING PROTECTION SAFETY** This symbol appears when substances used could stain or burn clothing.
	THERMAL SAFETY This symbol appears as a reminder to use caution when handling hot objects.		**FIRE SAFETY** This symbol appears when care should be taken around open flames.
	SHARP OBJECT SAFETY This symbol appears when a danger of cuts or punctures caused by the use of sharp objects exists.		**EXPLOSION SAFETY** This symbol appears when the misuse of chemicals could cause an explosion.
	FUME SAFETY This symbol appears when chemicals or chemical reactions could cause dangerous fumes.		**EYE SAFETY** This symbol appears when a danger to the eyes exists. Safety goggles should be worn when this symbol appears.
	ELECTRICAL SAFETY This symbol appears when care should be taken when using electrical equipment.		**POISON SAFETY** This symbol appears when poisonous substances are used.
	SKIN PROTECTION SAFETY This symbol appears when use of caustic chemicals might irritate the skin or when contact with microorganisms might transmit infection.		**CHEMICAL SAFETY** This symbol appears when chemicals used can cause burns or are poisonous if absorbed through the skin.

NAME _____ DATE _____ CLASS _____

Saving the Soil

Lab Preview

1. What will you do first? _____

   _____

2. What five methods can be used to control soil erosion? _____

   _____

You've seen eroded soil and you're probably aware of the problems erosion can cause. But how do you begin to explore how to solve these problems?

PROBLEM

Which of five methods is the best way to control soil erosion?

MATERIALS

5 aluminum 8- or 9-inch pie pans
leaves or grass clippings
500-mL beaker
water
metric ruler
newspaper
pebbles
potting soil
watering can
dishpan

SAFETY PRECAUTIONS

WHAT TO DO

1. Before you start, read the description of each model in Step 4 below, and decide which one you think will work best to solve the problem above. That method is your hypothesis, the answer you expect to get after you do the experiment.
2. Fill each pan almost to the rim with soil. Pat the soil until the surface is firm and flat. Soak the soil by pouring 100 mL of water into each pan.

3. Set one pan aside as the control for this experiment.
4. Use the other four pans to set up these conditions:
   a. Mulching: Cover the surface with a layer of grass clippings or leaves.
   b. Other soil cover: Tear the newspaper into small strips. Lay the strips across the surface, leaving about 5 mm between each strip.
   c. Terracing: Build two small walls of pebbles.
   d. Contour plowing: Use your finger to make a curved groove across the surface.
5. Follow this procedure with all five pans, starting with the control:
   a. Measure 200 mL of water into the watering can.
   b. Hold the pan so that one side touches the edge of the dishpan and the opposite edge is about 10 cm higher.
   c. Slowly pour the water onto the soil at the top of the pan. Wait until the excess water runs across the soil and into the dishpan. Note: Be sure to hold the terracing and contour plowing pans so the water runs across the pebble walls and the grooves.
   d. Pour the water and soil from each pie pan into the beaker. Measure it and record the results in a data table you construct in the space provided. When the soil settles to the bottom, measure and record its height in the beaker.
6. As a class, decide which method was most effective at preventing erosion.

Investigate Introduction

DATA AND OBSERVATIONS

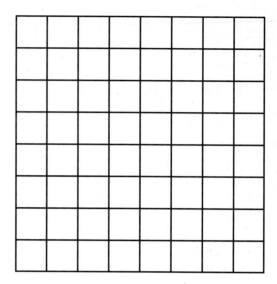

ANALYZING

1. In the space provided above, construct a graph to show results for all five pans. _____

_____

2. Compare and contrast the results for the pans. _____

_____

_____

CONCLUDING AND APPLYING

3. Was your hypothesis correct? _____

_____

_____

4. Going Further: One test or experiment isn't enough to prove a hypothesis. Most scientists perform numerous tests. Write an outline for another test of this hypothesis that does not use a model.

_____

_____

_____

6

NAME _____ DATE _____ CLASS _____

1-1 Using Contour Lines

Lab Preview

1. On what will you be marking the contour lines? _____

2. How will you create landform contours in the box? _____

   _____

How can a map show the shape of a landform? In the following activity, you will show the elevations of a landform by drawing contour lines, which are lines of equal elevation that show the shape of the landform.

PROBLEM

How can elevation of a landform be indicated on a map?

MATERIALS

metric ruler
clear plastic box and lid
model landform
water
transparency marker
transparency
tape
beaker

SAFETY PRECAUTIONS

WHAT TO DO

1. Using the ruler and the transparency marker, measure and mark 2-cm lines up the side of the box.
2. Secure the transparency to the outside of the box lid with tape.
3. Place the plastic model in the box. The bottom of the box will be zero elevation.
4. Using the beaker, pour water into the box to a height of 2 cm. Place the lid on the box.
5. Looking down at the top of the box, use the transparency marker to trace the top of the water line on the transparency.
6. Using the scale 2 cm = 5 ft, mark the elevation on the line.
7. Repeat Steps 4-6, adding water to the next 2-cm level and tracing until you have mapped the landform by means of contour lines.
8. Transfer the tracing of the contours of the landform onto paper.

Investigate 1-1 (continued)

ANALYZING

1. What is the contour interval of this contour map? _____

2. *Interpret* the relationship between contour lines on the map and the steepness of the slope on

   the landform. _____

   _____

   _____

3. Calculate the total elevation of the landform. _____

   _____

   _____

CONCLUDING AND APPLYING

4. How are elevations shown on topographic maps? _____

5. Explain whether all topographic maps must have a 0-ft elevation contour line. _____

   _____

   _____

6. **Going Further:** How would the contour interval of an area of steep mountains *compare* with the

   interval of an area of flat plains? _____

   _____

   _____

I N V E S T I G A T E !

2-1 Mirror Reflections

Lab Preview

1. What do you use to reflect a beam of light? _____

2. Where do you reflect the first light beam? _____

When you see light reflected from a mirror, you see an entire object—your head, a car, or a chair, for example. You probably don't think about what happens when light reflects in a mirror. You can easily discover how mirrors reflect light in this activity.

PROBLEM

How does light reflect in a mirror and how can this be used?

MATERIALS

4 pocket mirrors
flashlight
book

DATA AND OBSERVATIONS

Descriptions and Diagrams

WHAT TO DO

1. With a partner in a darkened room, use the mirrors and the flashlight to experiment with a beam of light.
2. Using as many mirrors as necessary, first reflect a light beam onto the ceiling.
3. Now, place a book upright on a desk.
4. Position the mirrors so that a light beam striking a mirror placed in front of the book is reflected to the back of the book.
5. Now, use your mirrors to reflect light into another room.
6. Using descriptions and diagrams, record the different positions of the mirrors, the flashlight, and the light beam for each trial in the space provided below and copy them *in your Journal.*

Investigate 2-1 (continued)

ANALYZING

1. Make a statement that tells how light is reflected from a mirror. _____

_____

2. What must you do to make the light beam change direction? _____

_____

3. If you reversed the positions of the flashlight and the point at which the reflected beam strikes an

object, how would the path of the light be affected? _____

_____

CONCLUDING AND APPLYING

4. When might it be necessary to bounce light with mirrors? Name some situations in which a

mirror would be more convenient than a light source. _____

_____

_____

5. *Predict* how you would arrange your flashlight and mirrors to get an image of the flashlight that
would continue to be reflected from one mirror to the other. Write your prediction *in your*

Journal and then try it. _____

_____

6. Going Further: Construct a periscope to see around corners or over fences using what you have
learned in this activity. Draw a diagram in the space provided below to show how the light enters

the periscope and reaches the viewer's eye. _____

_____

_____

_____

_____

DESIGN YOUR OWN
INVESTIGATION

2-2 Seeing Colors

Lab Preview

1. What color of paper will you use? _____

2. How many different colors will you use in this activity? _____

Think about the many things you see each day—flowers, the sky, the words and the photos on this page. Some things are easier to see than others, depending on the light, how far away from you it is, and the color.

PROBLEM
Which colors are easiest for human eyes to see? If you want the letter M to stand out from a given distance, does the color of the letter and the background affect your ability to see it?

FORM A HYPOTHESIS
Look at the photos on this page, then decide on a hypothesis predicting the easiest single color and combination of colors to see from a long distance.

OBJECTIVES
- Observe what color is easiest for most people to identify from a long distance.
- Compare and contrast color combinations for ease of identifying letters at a distance.
- Demonstrate that letters are easier to read against certain color backgrounds.

MATERIALS
scissors
glue, tape, or paper clips
posterboard and art paper of various colors
   including black and white

SAFETY PRECAUTIONS

Be careful when using scissors.

DATA AND OBSERVATIONS

Distance/Color				
m				
m				
m				
m				

Design Your Own Investigation 2-2 (continued)

PLAN THE EXPERIMENT

1. Look at the posterboard and paper. As a group decide what colors you will test for your hypothesis.
2. Discuss the best way to test your hypothesis, then write a procedure for the experiment. Make certain that colors are compared under the same conditions of distance and light.
3. Design a data table in your Science Journal or on a word processing program.
4. Determining which color or colors are easiest to identify is a judgment. Most people will agree on the easiest color to see, but perhaps

not everyone. To make your data more reliable, you need to test each color more than once. Ten people determining which color is easiest to identify gives stronger information than one person determining that color.

CHECK THE PLAN

1. Make certain your data table is designed to record each individual test.
2. Before you start the experiment, have your teacher approve your plan.
3. Carry out your experiment. Make observations and record your data.

ANALYZE AND CONCLUDE

1. **Interpreting Data** Was your hypothesis supported by the data? Use your data to explain why or why not. _____

_____

_____

2. **Using Numbers** In each experiment, add up and record the number of times a specific color was chosen as the easiest to see from a long distance away. What percentage of the time was this color chosen? Percentages are figured by dividing the number of times chosen by the total number of trials. Then multiply by one hundred and add a percent sign. Use your calculator.

_____

_____

3. **Using Numbers** Find what percentage of the time the most easily seen combination of colors was chosen in the tests. _____

4. **Interpreting Data** Using the percentages found in the questions above, write a conclusion about which colors and color combinations are easiest to see. _____

_____

GOING FURTHER

Inferring If you were designing a sign to be seen easily at a distance, what colors would you choose? Use your data to explain your choice. _____

_____

DESIGN YOUR OWN
INVESTIGATION

3-1 Length and Pitch

Chapter

3

Lab Preview

1. What will you be measuring in each test tube? _____

_____

2. How many test tubes will be completely empty? _____

You have learned that shortening the length of a guitar string speeds up the vibrations and raises the pitch of the sound. If you produce a sound by blowing across a test tube full of water, what happens to the pitch of that sound when you empty the tube to half full and blow across it?

PROBLEM
When air is blown across the top of a test tube, the column of air inside the tube vibrates. When water is added to the tube, what happens? How does this added water affect pitch?

FORM A HYPOTHESIS
Based on what you have learned about changing pitch, decide on a hypothesis for your group. Write it down.

OBJECTIVES
- Observe how pitch changes with varying amounts of water in the test tube.
- Conclude from your investigation how the length of the vibrated column of air affects pitch.

MATERIALS
test tubes with an approximate diameter of
   2.5 cm
test-tube rack
felt-tip marker
water
small graduated cylinder
metric ruler

SAFETY PRECAUTIONS

Be careful handling glass test tubes.

PLAN THE EXPERIMENT
1. Examine the materials and plan how your group will test the hypothesis. Write a step-by-step procedure.
2. In your Science Journal, draw diagrams of all the test tubes you use. Record your data on this diagram.
3. How will you measure the length of the column of air? Be sure to record the measurements on your diagram.

CHECK THE PLAN
1. Who will blow across the test tubes? Do the tubes need to be identical? Who will judge the sound? Do you need more than one person's opinion to judge the pitch?
2. Before you begin your experiment, make certain that your teacher approves your plan.
3. Carry out the experiment. Make observations and record your data on diagrams in your Science Journal.

Design Your Own Investigation 3-1 (continued)

ANALYZE AND CONCLUDE

1. Analyze Data Which test tube produced the lowest pitch? How much water was in it?

_____

_____

2. Which test tube produced the highest pitch? How much water was in it? _____

_____

_____

3. Compare and Contrast Compare the pitches of all the bottles. How did the amount of water in

the test tube affect the pitch of the vibrating column of air? _____

_____

4. Conclude Make a statement about how the length of a vibrating column of air affects its pitch.

_____

_____

5. Using Math From your diagram, construct a bar graph relating column size to pitch.

_____

_____

6. What basic musical instrument does your test-tube instrument resemble? _____

_____

GOING FURTHER

Can you create a musical scale by blowing across test tubes with varying amounts of water in them?

How many test tubes will you need to create a musical scale of one octave? _____

_____

I N V E S T I G A T E !

Text Page 104

Chapter 3

3-2 Length and Resonance

Lab Preview

1. How is a tuning fork's frequency measured? _____

2. What do you do to the tube in this activity to discover the loudest sound? _____

_____

A tabletop resonates with the frequency of a vibrating tuning fork. The body of a guitar resonates with its vibrating strings. In this experiment, investigate the resonance of the air inside a glass tube.

PROBLEM

Can you find the length of a tube of air that will resonate with a given sound frequency?

MATERIALS

2 tuning forks of different frequencies (256 Hz or higher)
1000-mL graduated cylinder (or bucket or pitcher about 30 cm deep)
metric ruler
plastic or glass tube, 2.5 cm in diameter, about 45 cm long, open at both ends
rubber mallet
water

WHAT TO DO

1. Copy the data table *in your Journal*.
2. Find the number and the letters Hz on your tuning fork and record them under *Tuning Fork Frequency* in the data table.
3. Fill the graduated cylinder or bucket with water.

4. Hold one end of the tube while you place the other end partway into the cylinder or bucket of water (see photo *A*, page 105 of your text).
5. Have your partner strike the tuning fork with the mallet and hold the fork over the tube.
6. Raise or lower the tube in the water until the loudest sound is produced.
7. Have your partner *measure* the distance from the top of the tube to the water's surface (see photo *B*, page 105 of your text). Record the length in the table. This is the length of the column of air that resonates with the vibration of the tuning fork.
8. Repeat Steps 5–7 for the second tuning fork.

DATA AND OBSERVATIONS

Tuning Fork Frequency	Length of the Column of Air

Investigate 3-2 (continued)

ANALYZING

1. *Interpret* your table to answer these questions. For which tuning fork is the length of the column of air longer? Which column of air resonates at the lower frequency? _____

_____

_____

2. How does the length of a column of air relate to its resonant frequency? _____

_____

_____

CONCLUDING AND APPLYING

3. Obtain a different frequency tuning fork by trading with another group. Look at its frequency and *predict* how the length of the column of air that resonates with this tuning fork will compare with your earlier trials. Record your prediction *in your Journal*. Repeat the experiment and see how your prediction compares with what you observe. _____

_____

_____

_____

4. **Going Further:** Have you ever heard an object in a room buzz when a certain note is played loudly on the radio? Explain what causes this to happen. _____

_____

_____

DESIGN YOUR OWN
INVESTIGATION

4-1 Elements, Compounds, Mixtures

Chapter
4

Lab Preview

1. How will you know an element? _____

2. Why is it important to NOT eat foods in an experiment in the lab? _____

_____

Developing a system of classification helps turn a definition into a tool for solving problems. For example, you can classify a vehicle as a car, pick-up truck, or van based on identifying characteristics. Can a similar system be made to distinguish among elements, compounds, and mixtures?

PROBLEM
How can their differences help you distinguish among elements, compounds, and mixtures?

FORM A HYPOTHESIS
Find the definitions of elements, compounds, and mixtures from your text. If you were classifying objects based on these definitions, what characteristics would you assign to an element? To a compound? To a mixture?

OBJECTIVES
- Define *element, compound, heterogeneous mixture*, and *homogeneous mixture.*
- Develop a list of identifying characteristics based on the definitions.
- Classify an object as an element, a compound, a heterogeneous mixture, or a homogeneous mixture.

POSSIBLE MATERIALS
small amount of rock salt
glass of lemonade
aluminum foil
baking soda
small piece of granite
copper wire
piece of graphite (carbon)
vinegar and oil salad dressing

SAFETY PRECAUTIONS

Never eat, drink, or taste anything used in a laboratory experiment.

PLAN THE EXPERIMENT
1. Work as a group to choose objects and agree on a hypothesis. Record in your Science Journal the identifying characteristics that you will look for as you classify the objects.
2. Design a data table in your Science Journal to record the names of your test objects and the classifications you assign them.

CHECK THE PLAN
1. Do your identifying characteristics correspond to the definitions of substances and mixtures?
2. How will you keep track of your observations and explanations?
3. Before you begin, have the teacher check your plan and your list of objects.
4. Carry out the experiment.

Design Your Own Investigation 4-1 (continued)

DATA AND OBSERVATIONS

Material	Element	Compound	Mixture	
			Homogeneous	Heterogeneous
Rock salt				
Lemonade				
Aluminum foil				
Baking soda				
Granite				
Copper wire				
Graphite				
Vinegar and oil				

ANALYZE AND CONCLUDE

1. Observe and Infer If you know the name of a substance, how can you find out if it is an element?

_____

2. Compare and Contrast How do compounds differ from mixtures? _____

_____

3. Classify What homogeneous mixtures did you identify? How did you determine the difference

between homogeneous and heterogeneous mixtures? _____

_____

4. Classify Did your list of identifying characteristics help you to correctly classify the objects?

How would you change your list if you were to repeat the experiment? _____

_____

5. Make and Use Tables Make a table that lists the four kinds of substances and mixtures, their
differences, and the classifications you made. Look in the Skill Handbook under Making Tables if

you need help. _____

GOING FURTHER

Use your list of identifying characteristics to classify the contents of your refrigerator at home. Identify

whether there are more substances or mixtures. _____

_____

<u>I N V E S T I G A T E !</u>   **Text Page 132** _____ Chapter 4

4-2   Using Density

Lab Preview

1. Why should you wear goggles when you are working with alcohol? _____

   _____

2. What mass will you measure first? _____

In this activity, you will find the density of three materials. You will use this information to help you identify an unknown material.

PROBLEM
How can density be used to identify an unknown material?

MATERIALS
water
rubbing alcohol
unknown (liquid) substance
100-mL graduated cylinder
saturated saltwater mixture
pan balance and set of masses
goggles

SAFETY PRECAUTIONS

Avoid open flames.

WHAT TO DO
1. Copy the data table *into your Journal.*
2. Use the balance to measure the mass, in grams, of a clean, dry graduated cylinder. Record the mass in your table.
3. Fill the cylinder with water to the 50-mL mark.
4. *Measure* the mass of the filled cylinder and record it in your table under the heading *Total Mass.* Then discard the water as directed by your teacher.
5. *Calculate* the mass of the water by subtracting the mass of the empty cylinder from the total mass. Record the result under the heading *Actual Mass.*
6. Repeat Steps 3–5, first using the salt water, then the rubbing alcohol, and finally the unknown material. **CAUTION:** *Alcohol burns readily, and its fumes can be irritating. Wear goggles. Be sure that the room is well-ventilated, and there are no open flames.*
7. Record the data for each material.

DATA AND OBSERVATIONS

Material	Mass of Cylinder	Total Mass	Actual Mass	Volume	Density (g/cm³)
Water				50 mL	
Salt water				50 mL	
Alcohol				50 mL	
Unknown				50 mL	

Investigate 4-2 (continued)

ANALYZING

1. *Calculate* the density for each material by dividing its actual mass by its volume. Round to two

   decimal places. _____

   _____

   _____

2. Which known material had the highest density? _____

CONCLUDING AND APPLYING

3. What was the unknown material? _____

   _____

   _____

4. How did finding the density of the unknown material help you identify it? _____

   _____

   _____

5. **Going Further:** What other physical properties might you also look for and measure in

   identifying materials? _____

   _____

I N V E S T I G A T E !

5-1 Evaporation and Solutions

Lab Preview

1. Why is it recommended to wear safety goggles in this activity? _____

   _____

2. What do you do with the string in this activity? _____

   _____

You've seen that solutions cannot be separated by letting them stand or by filtering. In this activity, you'll try to separate a solution using evaporation.

PROBLEM

Can solutions be separated by evaporation?

MATERIALS

safety goggles
Epsom salt (magnesium sulfate)
large beaker (400 mL)
thick, water-absorbent string
water
graduated cylinder (100 mL)
2 small beakers (250 mL)
spoon or stirring rod

SAFETY PRECAUTIONS

WHAT TO DO

1. Copy the data table *into your Journal.*
2. Put on your safety goggles. *Measure* 200 mL of water into a graduated cylinder and then pour this into the large beaker.
3. Dissolve as much Epsom salt as you can in the water. To do this, slowly add the solute to the water until some of the solute stays undissolved after stirring.
4. Fill the two small beakers with the Epsom-salt solution. Place them side by side about 10 cm apart. Drape the string between the beakers with the ends of the string submerged in the solutions. It should be set up as in the illustration (see photo *A,* page 159 of your text). The string should sag slightly between the beakers. Let the setup stand undisturbed for several days.
5. *Observe* the setup every few days and record your observations in your data table.

DATA AND OBSERVATIONS

Date	Observations	
	Beakers	String

Investigate 5-1 (continued)

ANALYZING

1. What happened to the water level in the beakers? Where did the water go? _____

_____

2. What happened on the string between the beakers? _____

_____

CONCLUDING AND APPLYING

3. *Predict* the effect of the following changes in the outcome of this Investigation.

   a. You dissolved only half as much Epsom salt in the water. _____

   _____

   b. No string was placed between the beakers. _____

4. Which part of a solid-liquid solution evaporated in the activity, the solute or the solvent? Which

   part was left behind? _____

5. **Going Further:** *Infer* why evaporation can't be used to separate gas-gas solutions. _____

_____

_____

5-2 Saturating a Solution at Different Temperatures

Chapter 5

Lab Preview

1. Explain the meaning of the safety symbols in this activity. _____

_____

_____

2. As you watch the sugar solution cool, how will you know when it reaches the saturation

temperature? _____

A solvent can dissolve only a certain amount of solute before it is saturated. However, changing the temperature changes the situation. The point of saturation is different for different temperatures.

PROBLEM

How does the solubility of table sugar in water change at different temperatures?

FORM A HYPOTHESIS

Form a hypothesis about whether there is a change in solubility for sugar when temperature is changed. How will solubility change when temperature changes?

OBJECTIVES

- Predict how the saturation point of a solution will change with differing temperatures.
- Measure the temperature at the saturation point for different solutions.

MATERIALS

a two-hole stopper containing a thermometer
    and a copper wire stirrer
large test tube
test-tube holder
distilled water
table sugar
graduated cylinder
laboratory balance
hot plate
beaker of water
safely goggles
oven mitt

SAFETY PRECAUTIONS

Be careful when using the hot plate and when inserting the stopper into the test tube.

DATA AND OBSERVATIONS

Grams of Sugar	mL of Water	Saturation Temperature (°C)	Grams of Sugar Per 100 g of Water
28.7	10		
28.7	12		
28.7	14		

Design Your Own Investigation 5-2 (continued)

PLAN THE EXPERIMENT

1. You will need to find the temperature at the saturation point for different solutions. The saturation point is reached when the solution cools enough that crystals of solute begin to form in the solution. If you begin with 28.7 g of sugar and 10 mL of water and run one test, how would you change the solution for another test? Would you add 2 mL of water? Would you add 2 g of sugar? In your group, decide how you will change the solution for each of three trials.

2. Copy the data table into your Science Journal and record the second and third solutions your group has agreed to test.

3. Set up the equipment as shown in the photo on page 168. How will you dissolve the sugar? You should not need to heat the solution to more than 80°C. How will you find the saturation point? Watch the temperature closely as the solution cools and you look for crystals.

CHECK THE PLAN

1. What will stay constant in the three trials? What will change?

2. Will you stir the contents of the tube while it heats? While it cools?

3. Before you start the experiment, have your teacher approve your plan.

4. Carry out your experiment. Make observations and complete your data table in your Science Journal.

ANALYZE AND CONCLUDE

1. **Use Math** Calculate the grams of sugar per 100 g of water at each saturation temperature. Use the following formula and insert the appropriate numbers for grams of sugar and milliliters of water from your data table.

$$\text{Mass of sugar} = \frac{?\text{ g sugar}}{?\text{ mL water}} \times 100 \text{ mL water}$$

_____

_____

2. **Measure in SI** What were the three saturation temperatures? _____

_____

3. **Compare and Contrast** How did the mass of sugar that dissolved in 100 g of water change as the

temperature changed? _____

4. **Hypothesize** Explain how your hypothesis was supported or disproved. _____

_____

5. **Use Graphs** Graph the solubility versus temperature for the sugar-water solution.

_____

GOING FURTHER

Predict the solubility of sugar at 0°C, the freezing point of water, and at 100°C, the boiling point of

water. _____

6-1 Identifying Acids and Bases

Lab Preview

1. What safety equipment will you use during this activity? _____

2. Predict which substances will be acidic. _____

_____

Acids and bases are used for different purposes. Their uses often correspond to the way they react to various substances. Litmus paper, which is red in the presence of an acid and blue in the presence of a base, can be used to identify acids and bases.

PROBLEM

How can acids and bases be identified?

FORM A HYPOTHESIS

As a group, form a hypothesis that will help you determine which substances are acids and which are bases.

OBJECTIVE

• Identify acids and bases based on their reactions with litmus paper.

POSSIBLE MATERIALS

test-tube rack
(6) test tubes
household ammonia
cola
table salt
lemon juice
vinegar
baking soda
orange slices
deodorant
piece of antacid tablet
red and blue litmus paper
stirring rods
distilled water

SAFETY PRECAUTIONS

Goggles and apron should be worn at all times when using these weak acids and bases. Do not allow the substances to contact your skin.

PLAN THE EXPERIMENT

1. Within your group, choose six of the available substances to test.
2. What procedure will you follow to test each substance? Will you use both kinds of litmus paper? Is it important to use clean stirring rods?
3. Water is a neutral liquid; it is neither acidic nor basic. How will you use it as you test the solids?
4. How will you keep track of your findings? In your Science Journal, design a table or chart to use during your experiment.

CHECK THE PLAN

1. Have another group read your plan after they have finished writing their own. Do they understand what you plan to do?
2. Before you begin, have your teacher approve your plan.
3. Carry out the experiment.

Design Your Own Investigation 6-1 (continued)

DATA AND OBSERVATIONS

Material tested	Effects on Litmus Paper		
	Red to Blue	Blue to Red	No Effect
Lemon juice			
Ammonia			
Distilled water			
Vinegar			
Cola			
Baking soda			
Table salt			
Orange slices			
Deodorant			
Antacid tablet			

ANALYZE AND CONCLUDE

1. Observe What changes did you observe for acids? For bases? _____

_____

2. Infer Which substances did you infer were acids? Bases? _____

_____

_____

3. Analyze How effective was your procedure? Are there things you would change if you were to do

it again? _____

4. Conclude List any substances that showed no change with the litmus test. What can you

determine about them? _____

_____

GOING FURTHER

Predict how the bases you identified in the Explore activity on page 193 would affect litmus paper.

_____

I N V E S T I G A T E !   Text Page 200   Chapter 6

6-2 Finding pH

Lab Preview

1. Why should you wear an apron during this activity? _____

_____

2. How much cabbage juice do you use for each test tube? _____

Certain substances change color when pH changes. A common substance of this type found in nature is red cabbage juice. In this Investigate, you will test the pH of household liquids using red cabbage juice.

PROBLEM

How can cabbage juice indicate the relative pH of acids and bases?

MATERIALS

safety goggles
7 test tubes
100-mL graduated cylinder
apron
test-tube rack
red cabbage juice
grease pencil
7 dropping bottles with: household ammonia, colorless carbonated soft drink, baking soda solution, sodium hydroxide solution, hydrochloric acid solution, distilled water, white vinegar

SAFETY PRECAUTIONS

Use caution when working with acids and bases. Wear lab aprons and goggles.

WHAT TO DO

1. *In your Journal,* make a data table in which you can record your prediction of pH, the color of the cabbage juice, and the relative pH of the acid or base for each of the seven solutions to be tested.

2. Wear an apron and goggles. Mark each test tube with the substance name.

3. Fill each test tube with 15 mL of the cabbage juice.

4. Use the following table of colors to predict the relative pH of the test solutions. Record these predictions in your table.

5. Add 5 drops of each test solution to the test tube labeled with its name. **CAUTION:** *If you spill any liquids on your skin, rinse the area immediately with water. Alert your teacher if any liquid is spilled in the work area.*

6. *Observe* any color changes of the cabbage juice. In your data table, record the color and relative pH of each solution.

Cabbage Juice Color	Relative pH
bright red	strong acid
red	medium acid
reddish purple	weak acid
purple	neutral
blue green	weak base
green	medium base
yellow	strong base

Investigate 6-2 (continued)

ANALYZING

1. *Classify* which test solutions were acids and which were bases. _____

_____

2. Which base was weakest? _____

3. Which acid was strongest? _____

4. *Infer* why distilled water didn't change the color of the cabbage juice. _____

_____

CONCLUDING AND APPLYING

5. How do your predictions *compare* with the results? _____

_____

_____

_____

6. How does cabbage juice indicate the relative strength of acids and bases? _____

_____

_____

_____

7. **Going Further:** *Predict* how other substances at home would react with the cabbage juice. Ask an

adult to help you test your predictions. _____

_____

_____

DESIGN YOUR OWN
INVESTIGATION

7-1 Living or Nonliving?

Lab Preview

1. In this activity, what is the food? _____

2. Why do you need a microscope in this activity? _____

_____

In this section, you have learned about the traits of living things. During this investigation, you will observe how substances react to food. Use your knowledge about living things to help you prove which substances are living.

PROBLEM
How can you prove that something is living or nonliving?

FORM A HYPOTHESIS
As a group, decide on a statement or prediction about whether yeast, baking soda, and salt are living or not. Record your hypothesis.

OBJECTIVES
- Observe the changes over time when something is fed.
- Compare the reactions of test items to the traits of living organisms.

POSSIBLE MATERIALS
microscope
coverslips
4 test tubes each with 20 drops of sugar water
1 package dry yeast
salt (NaCl)
baking soda (NaHCO$_3$)
measuring spoons
labels

SAFETY PRECAUTIONS

Dispose of the yeast as directed by your teacher.

PLAN THE EXPERIMENT
1. As a group, decide how you will test your hypothesis. Design the experiment to prove if any of the three test items are alive. Write down the steps of your experiment.
2. What are the variables? What is the control? Before you begin, label the tubes for your experiment and record what each one will contain. Make certain that you use the same amount of each substance in the tests. In this experiment, sugar water is the food.
3. Make a data table. In the table, list the traits of living things that you will observe.
4. Immediately after you put each test item into the sugar water, observe a sample of each under the microscope. At the end of the experiment, observe the samples again and compare.

CHECK THE PLAN
1. Investigations like this one take time. Plan to take observations every 10 minutes for 40 minutes. After every observation, record what you saw.
2. Before you start your experiment, make certain your teacher approves your plan.
3. Carry out the experiment.

Design Your Own Investigation 7-1 (continued)

DATA AND OBSERVATIONS

Time	A	B	C	D
After ____ minutes				
After ____ minutes				
After ____ minutes				
After ____ minutes				

ANALYZE AND CONCLUDE

1. **Observe** How did test tubes A, B, C, and D change over the time you observed them?

_____

2. **Infer** What was in the test tubes that changed? Was the change an indication of a life process

occurring? _____

3. **Conclude** What waste product was produced in the experiment? What do you think it is? Why

did it occur? _____

4. **Scientific Illustration** Make drawings of what you see under the microscope at the beginning

and at the end of the experiment for each tube. _____

_____

5. **Collect Data** In your data table, check off each trait that applies to each item tested.

_____

_____

_____

_____

6. **Conclude** Use your data to conclude whether each test item is living or nonliving.

_____

_____

GOING FURTHER

Design an experiment in which you test for each of the characteristics of life as described on pages

220 and 221. _____

I N V E S T I G A T E !

Text Page 236

Chapter 7

7-2 Using a Key

Lab Preview

1. What is a key? _____

_____

_____

2. How many species of jays could you identify with this key? _____

In this activity, you will learn to use a key to identify jay birds. A key is a step-by-step guide for identifying organisms that requires that you make a choice between two statements at each step until a name is reached for an organism.

PROBLEM

How is a key used to identify jays?

MATERIALS

paper and pencil

WHAT TO DO

1. Look at the two jays pictured on page 237 of your text.
2. Begin with Step 1 of the Key to Jays of North America. Select one statement that is true about that bird and follow the direction it takes you. Follow each succeeding step until you identify the bird by its scientific names. Use the key to classify the bird labeled A, on page 237 of your text.
3. Use the data table below to record the common and scientific names for the jay.
4. Now use the same procedure to classify the species of jay labeled B, on page 237 of your text.

KEY TO JAYS OF NORTH AMERICA

1a If the jay has a crest on the head, go to Step 2.
1b If the jay has no crest, go to Step 3.
2a If the jay's crest and upper body are mostly blue, it is a blue jay, *Cyanocitta cristata.*
2b If the jay's crest and upper body are brown or gray, it is a stellar's jay, *Cyanocitta stelleri.*
3a If the jay is mostly blue, go to Step 4.
3b If the jay has little or no blue, go to Step 6.
4a If the jay has a white throat, outlined in blue, it is a scrub jay, *Aphelocoma coerulescens.*
4b If the throat is not white, go to Step 5.
5a If the jay has a dark eye mask and gray breast, it is a gray-breasted jay, *Aphelocoma ultramarinus.*
5b If the jay has no eye mask and has a gray breast, it is a pinyon jay, *Gymnorhinus cyanocephalus.*
6a If the jay is mostly gray and has black and white head markings, it is a gray jay, *Perisoreus canadensis.*
6b If the jay is not gray, go to Step 7.
7a If the jay has a brilliant green body with some blue on the head, it is a green jay, *Cyanocorax yncas.*
7b If the jay has a plain brown body, it is a brown jay, *Cyanocorax moria.*

DATA AND OBSERVATIONS

Jay	Scientific Name	Common Name
A		
B		

Investigate 7-2 (continued)

ANALYZING

1. Using the key, how many species of jay can you infer are in North America? _____

2. How many genera can be identified with this key? _____

CONCLUDING AND APPLYING

3. How do you know that this key doesn't contain all the species of jays in the world? _____

_____

_____

4. Why wouldn't you be successful in identifying a robin using this key? _____

_____

_____

5. **Going Further:** Why wouldn't it be a good idea to begin in the middle of a key, instead of with

the first step? _____

_____

_____

_____

I N V E S T I G A T E !

8-1 Shapes of Viruses

Lab Preview

1. How many models of viruses will you make in this activity? _____

2. What does the first safety symbol mean? _____

_____

Viruses all contain similar structures and materials, yet they differ greatly in shape. In this activity, you can observe and make models of some viruses.

PROBLEM
How can you make a model of a virus?

MATERIALS
3.7 cm × 0.7 cm bolt
2 pieces #22-gauge wire, 14 cm long
pipe cleaners, cut in 2-cm lengths
2 nuts to fit bolt
polystyrene ball, 4.5 cm in diameter

SAFETY PRECAUTIONS

Be careful when working with wires.

WHAT TO DO

1. Look at the photographs of the viruses taken with an electron microscope on page 251 of your text. Then, study the drawings of the viruses in Figures *A* and *B* shown below. The drawing in Figure *A* represents a virus enlarged 260 000 times. The drawing in Figure *B* represents a flu virus enlarged 300 000 times.

2. Notice the parts in Figure *A* that are labeled. To make a model of the virus, attach two nuts onto a bolt and screw them on as far as you can.

3. Twist the wires around the bolt near the bottom. Make the wire as tight as you can. Fold the wire ends and bend them so that they look similar to the drawing.

4. Use the polystyrene ball and pipe cleaners to make a model of the flu virus in Figure *B*.

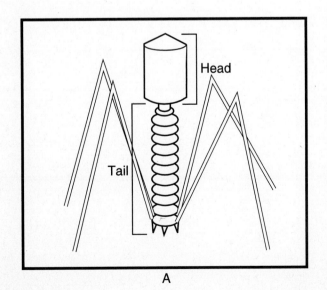

A

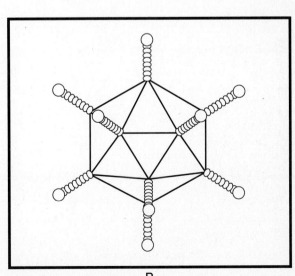

B

Investigate 8-1 (continued)

ANALYZING

1. *Compare* your models with Figures *A* and *B.* How are they alike? _____

_____

_____

2. *Contrast* the two viruses. How are they different from each other? _____

_____

_____

3. What is there about the structure of a virus that seems to help it get inside your cells?

_____

_____

CONCLUDING AND APPLYING

4. How does a virus differ from a cell? _____

_____

_____

5. **Going Further:** What kinds of illnesses have you heard of that are caused by viruses? *Make a table* of at least three diseases caused by viruses that you have researched in library references. In the table, list the disease, what it affects, and where it is found. You may want to use a computer

to make your table. _____

_____

_____

_____

8-2 The Work of Fungi

Lab Preview

1. What are the tiny threadlike branches of a mold called? _____

2. What foods will you use in your experiment? _____

Have you ever seen mold grow on fruit? When conditions are right, mold can cover and penetrate a fruit with hundreds of thousands of tiny threadlike branches called hyphae. The cells of hyphae release substances that break down organic materials in the fruit. Then bacteria move in, causing spoilage.

PROBLEM
Under what conditions does a mold grow best on fruit?

FORM A HYPOTHESIS
Has anyone in your group ever seen mold on fruit? As a group, discuss the conditions under which the mold grew. Then form a hypothesis that can be tested in your experiment.

OBJECTIVES
- Design an experiment using several variables to promote mold formation on fruit.
- Compare and contrast conditions that promote mold formation.
- Infer how certain conditions interact to promote or prevent the growth of mold.

POSSIBLE MATERIALS
peaches, apples, or oranges
paper towels
plastic bags
kitchen knife or fork
paper plate
water

SAFETY PRECAUTIONS

Be careful with knives if you decide to cut any fruit. Dispose of all moldy products as directed by your teacher.

PLAN THE EXPERIMENT
1. Examine the materials provided. Decide how you will use them in your experiment.
2. Design a procedure to test your hypothesis. Write down what you will do at each step.
3. How will you record your data? If you need a table, design one now in your Science Journal.

CHECK THE PLAN
1. List the conditions that you think will promote mold formation on fruit. Which condition will you test?
2. If you are testing more than one condition, have you allowed for a control in your experiment? What is the control?
3. Make sure your teacher approves your experiment before you proceed.
4. Carry out your experiment. Record your observations.

Design Your Own Investigation 8-2 (continued)

ANALYZE AND CONCLUDE

1. **Compare and Contrast** Which conditions promoted mold formation? Which conditions

   prevented mold formation? _____

   _____

   _____

2. **Recognize Cause and Effect** Was your hypothesis supported? If not, explain why it might still be

   right. _____

   _____

   _____

   _____

3. **Observe and Infer** On which fruits did mold grow the easiest? Suggest reasons for this.

   _____

   _____

   _____

4. **Infer** Suggest a good use for the moldy fruit at the end of this experiment instead of throwing it

   into the trash. Give a reason for your suggestion. _____

   _____

5. **Interpret Data** Based on the outcome of your experiment, what steps would you take to prevent

   oranges from molding quickly at home? _____

   _____

GOING FURTHER

You may have formed several hypotheses while designing this experiment. Test one of these
hypotheses or design a new experiment based on an observation made while conducting this one.

_____

_____

9-1 Picky Eaters

Lab Preview

1. What kinds of food will you feed to the mealworms in this activity? _____

   _____

2. How many times will you test the response of mealworms to different foods? _____

   _____

Are there certain foods that you do not like to eat? Maybe you don't like spinach because of its taste or texture. Other members of your family may not like corn. Do animals, like people, have food preferences? In the following activity, you will observe how mealworms respond to different kinds of food.

PROBLEM

How can you determine the food preferences of mealworms?

FORM A HYPOTHESIS

As a group, discuss the factors that might influence the mealworms' preference for one food over another, such as moistness or odor. Agree upon these factors, then form a hypothesis about the food that mealworms prefer.

OBJECTIVES

• Design an experiment that tests the mealworms' responses to various types of foods.

• Compare the mealworms' responses to different foods.

• Infer why mealworms prefer some foods over others.

POSSIBLE MATERIALS

20 mealworms
plastic storage box
pan balance
cheesecloth
20 g bran flakes
20 g dry oatmeal
20 g sugar-coated corn flakes
20 g broken, unsalted wheat crackers

gram masses
hand lens
forceps
water

SAFETY PRECAUTIONS

Return all mealworms to your teacher at the end of the experiment. Dispose of the cereals as directed by your teacher.

DATA AND OBSERVATIONS

Test Food	Day 1	Day 2	Day 3	Day 4
Oatmeal				
Corn Flakes				
Wheat Crackers				
Bran Flakes				

Design Your Own Investigation 9-1 (continued)

PLAN THE EXPERIMENT

1. Examine the materials. Which materials will you use? How will you use them?
2. Agree upon a way to test your hypothesis. Write down what you will do at each step.
3. Assign tasks to members of the group.
4. Design a table for recording your data. Decide when data will be measured and recorded.

CHECK THE PLAN

1. Determine where you will put the different foods in the plastic box. How will you calculate how much food the mealworms have eaten?

2. Decide where to place the mealworms in the box. Be sure to discuss how to move the mealworms back to their starting place so that the experiment can be repeated several times.
3. Before you start the experiment, have your teacher approve your plan.
4. Carry out your experiment. Complete your data table in your Science Journal.

ANALYZE AND CONCLUDE

1. **Use Numbers** Calculate the total number of mealworms that preferred each food.

_____

2. **Use Numbers** Calculate the mealworms' daily average of food intake for each food type.

_____

3. Which type of food did most mealworms prefer? Did this support your hypothesis? Explain.

_____

_____

_____

_____

4. Infer why the mealworms were attracted to a particular food. _____

_____

GOING FURTHER

Predict whether mealworms might be attracted to other food choices. Design an experiment to test

this prediction. Test the prediction. _____

_____

<u>**I N V E S T I G A T E !**</u> Text Page 300 _____ Chapter **9**

9-2 Earthworm Behavior

Lab Preview

1. How should you handle the worms during this experiment? _____

_____

2. Ideal conditions for an earthworm include moist earth. How might a worm react if there is

too much water? _____

_____

How can you determine the effect some conditions have on an earthworm? In this activity, you will observe some earthworm characteristics and infer how they enable the earthworms to survive.

PROBLEM
How is an earthworm adapted to live in soil?

MATERIALS
hand lens
vinegar
live earthworms in slightly moist soil
500 mL beaker
toothpick
flashlight
shallow pan
paper towels
cotton swab
water

SAFETY PRECAUTIONS

Earthworms can be released into the soil then you have completed your investigation. Earthworms are valuable because they aerate and mix soil as they move through it.

WHAT TO DO
1. Copy the data table *into your Journal.*
2. Open the container to be sure some of the earthworms are on the top of the soil. Shine the flashlight on the worms. Record how the worms react.
3. Moisten your hands and remove an earthworm from the container. **CAUTION:** *Use care when working with live animals.* Keep your hands moist while working with the earthworm. Hold the worm gently between your thumb and forefinger. Observe its movements and record them in the table.
4. Rub your fingers gently along the body. With a hand lens, *observe* the small hair-like bristles that you feel.
5. With the toothpick, gently touch the worm on the front and back ends. Record your observations.
6. Dip the cotton swab in vinegar. Place it in front of the worm on a wet paper towel. *Do not touch the worm with the vinegar.* Record what you observe.

DATA AND OBSERVATIONS

Condition	Response
Light	
Fingers	
Touch-front	
Touch-back	
Vinegar	

Investigate 9-2 (continued)

ANALYZING

1. What happens when light is shined on the earthworms? _____

_____

2. How does the earthworm react to touch? _____

_____

3. How does the earthworm react to the vinegar? _____

_____

CONCLUDING AND APPLYING

4. *Infer* how the earthworm's reaction to light is an adaptation for living in soil. _____

_____

_____

5. How are the bristles an adaptations for living in soil? _____

_____

_____

6. Going Further: *Design an experiment* to find out how the earthworm reacts to different

temperatures. _____

_____

_____

_____

DESIGN YOUR OWN
INVESTIGATION

10-1   They're All Wet

Lab Preview

1. What three seeds will you be working with in this activity? _____

_____

2. Where will you put the sprouting seeds? _____

You know that seed coats protect seeds, but a plant embryo cannot grow until this coat breaks open. In this activity, you will soak seeds in water to observe what effect this has on the seeds' coats. You will also observe whether soaking the seeds affects the time it takes them to sprout.

PROBLEM

How does soaking affect the time it takes seeds to sprout?

FORM A HYPOTHESIS

As a group, form a hypothesis about what might happen to seeds that are soaked in water for various lengths of time.

OBJECTIVES

- Predict the effect soaking has on the time it takes seeds to sprout.
- Infer what function water plays in the seeds' ability to sprout.

MATERIALS

6 small cups (paper or plastic)
12 radish seeds
12 watermelon seeds
12 bean seeds
paper towels

PLAN THE EXPERIMENT

1. Examine the materials provided by your teacher. Then design an experiment that uses these materials to test the effects of different soaking times on seeds.
2. Plan a data table in your Science Journal for recording your observations.
3. Because your test may last several weeks, assign daily tasks to all members of the group. Who will observe the seeds each day? Who will record the observations?

CHECK THE PLAN

Discuss and decide upon the following points and write them down.

1. Have you allowed for a control in your experiment? What is it?
2. How long will you conduct your test? How will you observe the sprouting seeds without injuring the seeds?
3. Make sure your teacher approves your experiment before you proceed.
4. Carry out your experiment. Record your observations.

Design Your Own Investigation 10-1 (continued)

ANALYZE AND CONCLUDE

1. Compare and Contrast Which seeds sprouted first? Last? _____

_____

_____

2. Infer What can you infer about the types of seeds and the times it took for them to sprout?

_____

_____

3. Separate and Control Variables Why did you soak the seeds for different amounts of time?

_____

_____

4. Interpret Data Infer what function water played in this experiment. _____

_____

_____

5. Draw a Conclusion How does soaking time affect the time it takes for a seed to begin growing?

Did your observations support your hypothesis? _____

_____

GOING FURTHER

Predict what would happen if you used tea or lemon juice as a soaking solution. _____

_____

_____

I N V E S T I G A T E !

10-2   Stomata

Lab Preview

1. What transparent outer tissue will you be removing from the lettuce leaf? _____

2. You will be observing how lettuce reacts to what two liquids? _____

You learned that stomata are openings through which oxygen, carbon dioxide, and water pass. In this activity, you will learn what stomata look like and how they work.

PROBLEM
How do stomata work?

MATERIALS
lettuce
water
microscope
salt solution
paper towel
dish
coverslip
microscope slide
forceps
pencil

SAFETY PRECAUTIONS
Use care handling the microscope.

WHAT TO DO
1. Copy the data table *into your Journal.*
2. From a dish of water containing lettuce leaves, choose a lettuce leaf that is stiff from absorbing the water.
3. Bend the leaf back and use the forceps to strip off some of the transparent tissue covering the leaf. This is the epidermis (see photo *A,* page 335 of your text).
4. Prepare a wet mount of a small section of this tissue (see photo *B,* page 335 of your text).
5. Examine the specimen under low and then high power of the microscope (see photo *C,* page 335 of your text). Draw and label the leaf section in your data table.
6. *Observe* the location and spacing of the stomata. Count how many of the stomata are open.
7. Place a paper towel at the edge of the coverslip and draw out the water. Using a dropper, add a few drops of salt solution at the edge of the coverslip. The salt solution will spread out beneath the coverslip.
8. Examine the preparation under low and then high power of the microscope. Draw and label the leaf section in your data table.
9. Repeat step 6.

DATA AND OBSERVATIONS

	Water Mount	Salt Solution
Number of stomata		
Spacing of stomata		
Drawing of leaf section		

Investigate 10-2 (continued)

ANALYZING

1. *Describe* the guard cells around a stoma. _____

_____

2. How many stomata did you see in each leaf preparation? _____

_____

_____

3. *Calculate* the percentage of the stomata open in water and in salt water. Which type of water had a higher percentage of open stomata? Which had a lower percentage of open stomata?

_____

_____

_____

_____

CONCLUDING AND APPLYING

4. *Infer* why the lettuce leaf became stiff in water. _____

_____

5. *Infer* why more stomata were closed in the salt solution. _____

_____

_____

6. Going Further: *Predict* what would happen if you soaked the lettuce in a stronger salt solution.

Would more or fewer stomata close? _____

_____

_____

I N V E S T I G A T E !

Text Page 354

Chapter **11**

11-1 What Do Owls Eat?

Lab Preview

1. What will you do first? _____

2. What does the second safety symbol mean? _____

_____

Owl pellets are made of the things an owl has swallowed, including fur and bones, that the owl is unable to digest. These pellets form in an owl's stomach and then the owl coughs them up. Examining an owl pellet can tell you much about what is going on in a small part of the owl's ecosystem.

PROBLEM

What role do owls play in their ecosystem?

MATERIALS

water	bowl
forceps	glass slide
coverslip	light microscope
magnifying glass	owl pellet
cardboard	glue

SAFETY PRECAUTIONS

Use care when handling microscope slides and coverslips. Dispose of all materials properly.

WHAT TO DO

1. With your group design a way to investigate what an owl pellet is made of and what its contents are. You should make a display of the contents of the owl pellet. After your plan has been approved by your teacher, carry it out.

2. *In your Journal,* write a short summary of your design and of what you found the contents of the owl pellet to be. Use the drawings on this page to help you identify the contents of the owl pellet.

Owl Pellet Contents				
Leg bone	Rib	Mammal skull	Bird skull	Mammal Jawbone

DATA AND OBSERVATIONS

List or sketch contents of the owl pellet.

Investigate 11-1 (continued)

ANALYZING

1. What made up the outside of the owl pellet? _____

_____

2. What did you see inside the pellet? How many of each kind of thing were there? _____

_____

3. What role does an owl play in its ecosystem? Is it a producer or a consumer? How do you know?

_____

_____

4. Describe the niche of an owl. Include where the owl lives, when it feeds, and what it eats.

   Describe the niche of an owl's prey. How are the two similar? How do they differ? _____

_____

_____

_____

_____

CONCLUDING AND APPLYING

5. If one owl pellet is produced each day, *estimate* the number of organisms eaten by the owl in a single day. Estimate the number of organisms an owl needs to eat to survive for one year.

_____

_____

_____

6. Going Further: *Design an experiment* to figure out what might happen to the population of owls

   if there were a sudden population explosion in mice. _____

_____

DESIGN YOUR OWN
INVESTIGATION

11-2   How Do Molds Grow?

Lab Preview

1. How many foods will you use? _____

2. How will you add the mold to the food? _____

Molds are fungi that can feed on just about anything. Think about where molds grow in our environment. Do they grow everywhere or are there factors that limit the growth of molds?

PROBLEM
What basic factor limits the growth of molds?

FORM A HYPOTHESIS
As a group, make a hypothesis about what factor seems most important in encouraging the growth of mold.

OBJECTIVES
- Identify factors that encourage growth of mold.
- Evaluate data.
- Determine which factor is a strong limiting factor to the growth of mold.

POSSIBLE MATERIALS
6 small paper cups
hand lens
labels
mold source
   (teacher supplies)
spray bottle of water
plastic wrap

cotton swabs
dry potato flakes
dry macaroni
sugarless, dry cereal
other dry saltless,
   sugarless food

SAFETY PRECAUTIONS

After transferring the mold source, wash your hands thoroughly. All surfaces in the experiment in touch with microorganisms should also be washed thoroughly. Do not inhale, taste, or touch material from the mold source. If you have a mold allergy, do not handle the mold.

PLAN THE EXPERIMENT
1. Examine the materials provided and decide how you will use them to test the group's hypothesis.
2. What is the limiting factor that you are testing? How will it be introduced in the experiment?
3. A small amount of food at the bottom of each cup is enough to feed mold. To introduce mold into each cup, rub a moist cotton swab across the dish of growing mold, then rub the cotton swab across the surface of the food in each cup. Try to put the same amount in each cup.
4. Mold grows over a period of days. Checking mold growth day by day should be taken into account in making your plan and your data table.

A

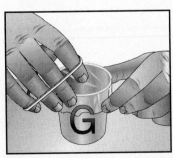

B

Design Your Own Investigation 11-2 (continued)

DATA AND OBSERVATIONS

Cup Contents		Day 1	Day 2	Day 3	Day 4
	A				
	B				
	C				
	D				
	E				
	F				
	G				
	H				

CHECK THE PLAN

1. How will you keep the environment in your experimental cups from change or contamination?
2. Where will you keep your experiment? Is it a neutral environment? Are the conditions for all the cups the same?
3. How long do you think it will take the mold to grow? How often will you check the experiment? Make certain that each observation is recorded in your data table.
4. Before your begin the experiment, have it approved by your teacher.
5. Carry out your experiment and record your data.

ANALYZE AND CONCLUDE

1. **Compare and Contrast** In which cups did you see evidence of mold growth? In which cups was there no mold growth? _____

2. **Infer** Determine whether there is a factor that limits the growth of mold. _____

3. **Interpret Data** Did mold grow faster on one particular food? _____

_____

4. **Draw a Conclusion** If you wanted to package food to sell, what is one way you could prevent

mold from spoiling your product? _____

_____

GOING FURTHER

Moisture is a limiting factor in mold growth. What other factors can you test to see if they limit

mold growth? _____

DESIGN YOUR OWN

INVESTIGATION

12-1 Average Walking Speed

Chapter

12

Lab Preview

1. Where will you conduct your walking tests? _____

2. What will you use to time each test? _____

When you walk, do you feel more comfortable walking barefoot, in sandals, or in athletic shoes designed for walking or running? Have you ever wondered what your average speed is when you walk?

PROBLEM

Can the type of foot gear you wear increase your average walking speed?

FORM A HYPOTHESIS

As a group, form a hypothesis predicting what foot gear will increase average walking speed for each individual in your group.

OBJECTIVES

- Measure speed and find averages for each individual.
- Compare foot gear for walking speed.
- Graph and interpret your data.

MATERIALS

meterstick
masking tape
stopwatch
shoes, boots, and sandals

PLAN THE EXPERIMENT

1. This is a group activity. Each group should test its hypothesis by designing a test procedure. Write it out step by step.

2. Speed is measured in meters per second (m/s). To find average speed, you need to know the distance traveled and the length of time each individual walked.

3. A walkway of a definite size is needed to conduct tests of the hypotheses. How long will your test track be?

4. How many trials will you conduct for each individual wearing a particular type of shoe? Testing someone 5 times is more reliable than testing once.

5. What foot gear will each individual wear? Should all the individuals tested by one group wear similar foot gear? Make certain that shoes, boots, and sandals are free from mud and dirt.

6. Design data tables in your Science Journal or on a spreadsheet for recording your data.

CHECK THE PLAN

1. What is your control in this test?
2. What are your variables?
3. Who will collect the data?
4. Make certain your teacher approves your plan before you proceed.
5. Carry out the experiment, make observations, and record the data.

Design Your Own Investigation 12-1 (continued)

ANALYZE AND CONCLUDE

1. **Analyze** Was your hypothesis supported by the data? Use your data to explain why or why not.

_____

_____

_____

_____

2. **Interpret** What foot gear produced the fastest average speeds in your group? _____

_____

3. **Analyze** Use all the class data to make bar graphs of individual speeds in each type of foot gear. This can be done on a spreadsheet. When you have a graph for each type of foot gear, analyze each one to find out who was the fastest walker in all the different shoes. Was there a foot gear

that caused some individual to walk slower while others walked faster? _____

_____

_____

_____

4. **Infer** What would happen to your average walking speed if your running shoes had wet mud on

them or they were worn down? _____

_____

_____

GOING FURTHER

If you have a suitable track, test which brand of running shoe increases average speed the most.

_____

_____

I N V E S T I G A T E !   **Text Page 398** — Chapter **12**

12-2   Instantaneous Acceleration

Lab Preview

1. What part of the accelerometer will you be observing to measure instantaneous acceleration?

   _____

2. What data will you record from the protractor? _____

Have you ever wondered how quickly you can accelerate? You can make an accelerometer that will allow you to measure the instantaneous acceleration of moving objects.

PROBLEM

How can you measure instantaneous acceleration?

MATERIALS

protractor
10 to 12 cm length of string
heavy button

Conversion Chart	
Moving Object	**Acceleration m/s/s**
90°	0
80°	1.7
70°	3.6
60°	5.7
50°	8.2
45°	9.8
40°	12
30°	17
20°	27
10°	56
0°	—

WHAT TO DO

1. Copy the data table *into your Journal*.
2. Assemble the materials as shown in the picture on page 399 of your text.
3. Hold the protractor upside down. The string should line up with the 90-degree mark on the protractor. When taking a reading, hold the protractor level.
4. Hold the accelerator at arm's length in front of your face with the numbers facing you. Quickly move the accelerometer to one side. Observe the angle of the string measured by the protractor. In what direction does the string move? What can you infer about the direction of acceleration? Try moving the accelerometer to the other side. What does this tell you?
5. Use the conversion chart to convert the angle reading on the accelerometer to an acceleration in meters per second per second.
6. Hold the accelerometer level and begin to run. Have a friend run with you and read the angle. Enter this data in the table.

DATA AND OBSERVATIONS

Moving Object	Acceleration m/s/s

Investigate 12-2 (continued)

ANALYZING

1. In what direction does the string move in comparison with the direction you move when you

speed up? Describe. _____

_____

_____

2. How did the string behave as you slowed down? _____

_____

_____

CONCLUDING AND APPLYING

3. Describe the position of the string while you were moving with constant velocity. _____

_____

_____

4. **Going Further:** Predict whether or not loose objects in a car would tend to move in the same

direction of the string, or in the opposite direction. _____

_____

_____

I N V E S T I G A T E !

Text Page 416

Chapter **13**

13-1 Acceleration of Falling Objects

Lab Preview

1. How do you calculate the distance from one image to the next? _____

_____

2. How many images of the ball are there in this activity? _____

Two falling balls in Figure 13-2 on page 416 of your text were recorded by strobe photography. Ten photographs were taken each second, each 1/10 of a second apart. Even though the balls are of different masses, they are falling at the same rate. Figure 13-2 is a drawing made from that photograph. At one side of the figure is a two-meter measuring stick. As each ball falls, there seems to be more distance between each succeeding image. You learned in Chapter 12 that distance traveled in a given time is a measure of speed. Therefore, if the balls are moving greater distances in the same period of time, they are speeding up or accelerating. Use Figure 13-2 to discover the acceleration of these two falling objects.

PROBLEM

What is the acceleration of falling objects?

MATERIALS

ruler
data table
Figure 13-2

WHAT TO DO

1. Copy the data table *into your Journal.*
2. Using the ruler as a guide, record the position of the first image of one ball as it

starts to fall. Always *measure* the ball position from the same point on the ball.
3. Record the position of the second image.
4. *Calculate* the distance from the first to the second image by subtracting the position of the first image from the position of the second image. Record this distance in the table under Image 2.
5. The images were taken 1/10 of a second apart. Use this information to *calculate* the average velocity of the balls between the first and second image in meter per second by dividing the distance fallen (in meters) by 1/10 second.
6. Record the position of the rest of the images. Make sure you always measure to the same place on the ball.
7. Find the distance between each pair of images and the average velocity. Fill these in for the rest of the images.
8. The last column of the table shows the exact time the balls' velocity reached the average velocity. To calculate these times, we assumed the clock started at the time of the first image and that the ball reached average velocity halfway in time between any two images.

55

Investigate 13-1 (continued)

DATA AND OBSERVATIONS

Image	Position (cm)	Distance Fallen (cm)	Average Velocity (m/s)	Time (S)
1				
2				0.10
3				0.20
4				0.30
5				0.40
6				0.50

ANALYZING

1. Did the velocity of the balls change as they fell? How do you know? _____

_____

2. Make a bar graph of your data. *Infer* what the bar graph tells about the position of the balls as

they fall. _____

_____

CONCLUDING AND APPLYING

3. How much did the average velocity increase between the second and third images? Between the

third and fourth images? _____

_____

4. Going Further: *Calculate* the balls' acceleration. Find the acceleration between the image at 0.10 s and the image at 0.30 s by dividing the increase in velocity by the time interval in seconds. What

was your result? _____

_____

DESIGN YOUR OWN
INVESTIGATION

13-2 The Period of a Pendulum

Lab Preview

1. What will you use to make a pendulum? _____

2. What string lengths will you be using? _____

A classic example of periodic motion is a pendulum in a grandfather clock. How does a pendulum help a clock keep time? What variables affect a pendulum's motion?

PROBLEM
What affects the period of a pendulum?

FORM A HYPOTHESIS
Think about the length of the pendulum, the bob mass, and amplitude (pull-back distance) of the pendulum. How do you think changing these variables will affect the period of the pendulum?

OBJECTIVES
• Separate and control variables in an experiment.
• Predict the effect of different tests on the period of a pendulum.

MATERIALS
ruler
string
masking tape
meterstick
metal washers
seconds timer

PLAN THE EXPERIMENT
1. Using the photo as a guide, explain how you will make your pendulum.
2. How will you measure the different variables?
3. Decide how you will vary each trial. The sample data tables will help guide you in your testing. Be sure you change only one variable in each trial.

CHECK THE PLAN
1. Prepare data tables in your Science Journal that are specific to your tests.
2. Have your teacher check your plan before you begin your experiment.

DATA AND OBSERVATIONS

Trial A		
Length = ___ cm		Mass ___ washers
Pullback Distance (cm)	Time for 10 Swings (s)	Pendulum Period (s)

Design Your Own Investigation 13-2 (continued)

Trial B		
Amplitude = ___ cm	Length = ___ cm	
Pendulum Bob Weight (Number of Washers)	Time for 10 Swings (s)	Pendulum Period (s)

Trial C		
Amplitude = ___ cm	Mass ___ washers	
Pendulum Length	Time for 10 Swings (s)	Pendulum Period (s)

ANALYZE AND CONCLUDE

1. **Compare** Summarize the results of your experiment and compare them with your hypothesis.

_____

2. **Explain** Looking back at your comparison in the last question, explain the effect of changing the

pendulum's bob mass, amplitude, and length on the pendulum period. _____

_____

3. **Use Numbers** Draw a graph plotting the pendulum's period for the different string length. Using
your graph, predict the pendulum's period for a string of 100 cm. What is the relationship

between the change in length of string and the change in period? _____

_____

GOING FURTHER

If you were building a pendulum clock, how would you build it to make sure the clock would be as

accurate as possible? _____

_____

I N V E S T I G A T E !

14-1 Differences in Streams

Lab Preview

1. How do you adjust the supply of water in this activity? _____

_____

2. What will you do to the sand in the stream table before trying each plan you develop?

_____

You've seen how streams form, but do streams have different characteristics? During this Investigate you will make your own model of streams.

PROBLEM

What factors do you think control stream characteristics? Think about what you know about streams. How would you make your own streams? How can you control the flow?

MATERIALS

2 pails
plastic hose
2 screw clamps
stream table
sand
blocks of wood

SAFETY PRECAUTIONS

Wear an apron to protect your clothing.

WHAT TO DO

Work with your group and plan ways to set up your stream table to form different streams. Show your plan to your teacher. If you are advised to revise your plan, be sure to check with your teacher again before you begin. Carry out your plan keeping in mind:

1. When you set up the stream table, dampen the sand.

2. By using a screw clamp on the supply hose, you can adjust the flow of water.

3. Do not make the reservoir end higher than the other end of the stream table.

4. Smooth out the sloping sand from the previous channel before forming another one.

Investigate 14-1 (continued)

ANALYZING

1. How could the flow of water be increased? _____

2. How could the flow of water from the supply pail be slowed down? _____

_____

3. Describe the channel that was formed when the sand end was high. _____

4. Describe the channel that was formed when the sand end was lower. _____

CONCLUDING AND APPLYING

5. *Compare and contrast* the two types of stream channels. _____

_____

_____

_____

6. *Determine the cause* of the differences between the two channels you made. _____

_____

_____

_____

7. Going Further: What kind of stream channels would you expect to form on plains? What kind

form in mountainous areas? _____

_____

_____

DESIGN YOUR OWN
INVESTIGATION

14-2 Ground Permeability

Chapter
14

Lab Preview

1. How many soil samples will you be testing? _____

2. Why do you need a watch with a second hand in this activity? _____

_____

There are many different kinds of soils. Soils that have a lot of connecting pores are characterized as permeable. Permeability affects how fast water can seep into the soil and flows through the ground.

PROBLEM
What factors determine how fast water seeps into different soils?

FORM A HYPOTHESIS
As a group, discuss what factors might influence the permeability of different soils. Agree upon these factors, then make a hypothesis that can be tested in your investigation.

OBJECTIVES
- Predict and compare the permeability of different soils.
- Measure the time it takes for water to seep into different soils.

- Infer why some soils are more permeable than others.

MATERIALS
watch with second hand
25-mL graduated cylinder
600-mL beakers (4)
water
metric ruler
permanent markers
potting soil, clay, sand, gravel

PLAN THE EXPERIMENT
1. Examine the materials provided by your teacher. Decide which materials you will use and how you will use them in your experiment.
2. Design a procedure to test your hypothesis. Write down what you will do at each step of your test.
3. Design a table for recording data.

DATA AND OBSERVATIONS

Soil Combinations	Observations of Soil	Prediction	Amount of Time to Sink In

Design Your Own Investigation 14-2 (continued)

CHECK THE PLAN

1. Review how you will combine the different materials to create "test soils." Will your combinations create different-colored and -textured test soils?

2. Have you determined how you will measure the water as it seeps into the soil?

3. Before you start the experiment, have your teacher approve your plan.

4. Carry out your experiment. Complete your data table in your Science Journal or on a computer shreadsheet.

ANALYZE AND CONCLUDE

1. Measure Measure the time it takes for the water in the beaker to permeate the soil. Compare your observations with your hypothesis and your predictions, and record these in your data table.

_____

2. Interpret Data Which of the soils was least permeable? Most permeable? How did you tell?

_____

_____

_____

3. Infer Infer why some soils are more permeable than others. _____

_____

_____

GOING FURTHER

Explain how permeability affects groundwater flow. Be sure to discuss runoff in your answer.

_____

_____

_____

DESIGN YOUR OWN

INVESTIGATION

15-1   Stream Erosion and Deposition

Lab Preview

1. How many trials will you run in this activity? _____

2. In this activity, how will you use the block of wood? _____

Streams are very effective movers of sediment. They can erode large quantities of sediment from an area and deposit them many miles away. But how do streams erode and deposit sediment, and where in the stream channel do these two processes take place?

PROBLEM

Which factors affect the way a stream erodes and deposits sediments?

FORM A HYPOTHESIS

As a group, list the factors that might influence stream erosion and deposition. Agree upon these factors, then form a hypothesis that can be tested in your experiment.

OBJECTIVES

- Design an experiment that tests the effects of different factors on stream erosion and deposition.
- Compare how different factors affect the way a stream erodes and deposits sediment.
- Determine where erosion and deposition occur in the stream channel.

DATA AND OBSERVATIONS

MATERIALS

stream table
sand, small pebbles, soil
plastic hose
screw clamps
pails with water
block of wood

SAFETY

PLAN THE EXPERIMENT

1. Examine the materials provided by your teacher. Determine how you will use these materials to create a stream channel.
2. Agree upon a way to test your hypothesis. Write down what you will do at each step.
3. Design a table for recording your data.

Design Your Own Investigation 15-1 (continued)

CHECK THE PLAN

1. How many factors will you test to observe stream erosion and deposition? Keep in mind that you should only test one factor or variable at a time.
2. If you are testing more than one variable, how will you ensure that the same conditions exist in the stream channel for each test?

3. Before you start the experiment, have your teacher approve your plan.
4. Carry out your experiment. Complete your data table in your Science Journal.

ANALYZE AND CONCLUDE

1. **Observe** Describe what happened to the stream channel in your tests. Where did most erosion

take place? Where did deposition occur? _____

_____

_____

2. **Conclude** What happened to the eroded materials? Describe how they were deposited.

_____

_____

_____

3. **Compare and Contrast** Compare the effects of different factors on stream erosion and deposition.

_____

_____

_____

4. Explain how your results support or do not support your hypothesis. _____

_____

_____

GOING FURTHER

Based on your observations, infer where the greatest amount of sediment might be found along a

river's course. _____

_____

I N V E S T I G A T E !

Text Page 488

Chapter 15

15-2 How Do Glaciers Change the Land?

Lab Preview

1. What shape river channel will you be making in this activity? _____

2. What electrical equipment will you need to use carefully? _____

Glaciers erode the land and can change it a great deal. In this activity, you'll observe how glaciers change the land as they erode Earth's surface.

PROBLEM

How do valley glaciers affect Earth's surface?

MATERIALS

ice block about 5 cm by 20 cm by 2 cm, containing sand, clay, and gravel
stream table with sand
lamp with reflector
metric ruler

SAFETY PRECAUTIONS

You will be using electrical equipment near water in this Investigate. Please keep these items apart from one another.

WHAT TO DO

1. Copy the data table *into your Journal.* Then set up the stream table and lamp as shown in the photo on page 488 of your text.
2. The ice block is made by mixing water with sand, gravel, and clay in a container and then freezing (see photo *A,* page 489 of your text).
3. Make a V-shaped river channel. Measure and record its width and depth. Draw a sketch that includes these measurements (see photo *B,* page 489 of your text).
4. Place the ice block, to act as a moving glacier, at the upper end of the stream table.
5. Gently push the glacier along the river channel until it's under the light, halfway between the top and bottom of the stream table.
6. Turn on the light and allow the ice to melt. *Observe* and record what happens.
7. *Measure* and record the width and depth of the glacial channel. Draw a sketch of the channel and include these measurements *in your Journal.*

DATA AND OBSERVATIONS

	Width	Depth	Observation
River			
Glacier			

Investigate 15-2 (continued)

ANALYZING

1. How can you *infer* the direction from which a glacier traveled? _____

_____

_____

_____

2. How can you tell how far down the valley the glacier traveled? _____

_____

_____

_____

CONCLUDING AND APPLYING

3. Determine the effect valley glaciers have on the surface over which they move. _____

_____

_____

_____

4. Going Further: How can you identify land that was once covered by a glacier? _____

_____

_____

_____

DESIGN YOUR OWN
INVESTIGATION

16-1 Succession

Chapter
16

Lab Preview

1. What do you put in the jar? _____

2. How many times will you take samples from the jar? _____

How does a newly dug pond differ from one that has existed for years? In this investigation, you'll simulate a pond-water ecosystem to explore succession and to discover how new ponds fill with a variety of organisms.

PROBLEM
How does a pond-water ecosystem change?

FORM A HYPOTHESIS
As a group, write out a statement that predicts what will happen to the populations of organisms in a new pond-water ecosystem. Include in your hypothesis changes you might expect in color, smell, and other characteristics of the water.

OBJECTIVES
- Predict what happens in the succession of a pond-water ecosystem.
- Observe and explain changes in the ecosystem.

MATERIALS
large, clean jar and lid
dried pond vegetation or pond water
distilled water
eyedroppers
microscope, slides, and coverslips

SAFETY PRECAUTIONS
Wash your hands after handling the materials in this investigation.

PLAN THE EXPERIMENT
1. Examine the materials provided. Decide how to use them to make a pond-water ecosystem.
2. How long will you conduct your investigation? How will you make observations? How often will you make observations?
3. What will you be observing? Some things to observe are water color, cloudiness, odor, sediment, and other factors that may change. Microscopically, look for organisms seen below. Record how the number of organisms increases or decreases.
4. Design a data table in your Science Journal.

CHECK THE PLAN
1. How will you know when one organism increases and another decreases?
2. Make sure you have a variable and a control.
3. Make sure your teacher approves your plan before you proceed.
4. Carry out the investigation. Record your observations.

Daphnia   *Hydra*   *Euglena*   *Paramecium*   *Rotifer*   *Spirogyra*   *Volvox*   *Anabaena*

Design Your Own Investigation 16-1 (continued)

DATA AND OBSERVATIONS

Day	Notes	Sketches
1		
2		
3		
4		

ANALYZE AND CONCLUDE

1. **Infer** What was the source of the organisms in the pond-water ecosystem? _____

_____

2. **Observe** What changes occurred that were observable without a microscope? _____

_____

_____

3. **Observe** What changes occurred that were observable with a microscope? _____

_____

4. **Observe** How many different organisms did you observe the first day? The last day?

_____

5. **Compare and Contrast** Did any of the organisms increase in number? Decrease? Explain how this may have occurred by making a general statement about succession that explains what

happened in your pond ecosystem. _____

_____

_____

_____

_____

GOING FURTHER

Work in small groups to produce rough graphs that reflect the relative changes in the populations of

organisms that you observed. What kind of graph would be best to use? _____

_____

I N V E S T I G A T E !   Text Page 514

Chapter **16**

16-2   Getting Up-Close and Personal

Lab Preview

1. How many organisms will you identify in the ecosystem? _____

2. What will you use to study the organisms? _____

Could you survive on a deserted island? Not without food! To get food you'd have to interact with other organisms in the ecosystem. In this activity, you'll find out more about how organisms in an ecosystem interact with one another.

PROBLEM

How do certain organisms interact in an ecosystem?

MATERIALS

Journal
hand lens or binoculars

WHAT TO DO

1. Choose an ecosystem near your school or home. It might be in a cluster of trees, a rotting log, a pond, a patch of weeds, or another setting.

DATA AND OBSERVATIONS

2. Identify at least two organisms that are interacting within this ecosystem. You can include organisms that are not always present, but leave evidence of their interaction through tracks or feathers.

3. In the space below and *in your Journal*, create a table to record and date your observations.

4. Over the next week, plan as many observations as possible. Schedule them for different times of the day.

5. Use a hand lens and/or binoculars to study the organisms you chose. Be sure to record *in your Journal* how these organisms interact with each other and with the environment.

Investigate 16-2 (continued)

ANALYZING

1. Describes the environment of your ecosystem. _____

_____

_____

2. **Spreadsheet** List all the populations of organisms present in the ecosystem. Put these data on

your spreadsheet. _____

_____

_____

3. Which organisms did you study? Are they producers, consumers, or decomposers? _____

_____

_____

4. What evidence did you find of competition within the ecosystem? Cooperation? Interaction

between organisms and their environment? _____

_____

_____

CONCLUDING AND APPLYING

5. What did each organism you studied do that helped it survive? _____

_____

6. What might happen if one or both of the organisms you studied disappeared from this ecosystem?

In what ways would the ecosystem be affected? _____

_____

7. **Going Further:** Think of a change you could make in this ecosystem that would not deliberately
damage it. **Predict** how the two organisms you studied would react to the change you suggest.

Then, test your prediction. _____

_____

_____

_____

DESIGN YOUR OWN
INVESTIGATION

17-1 Waves on a Coiled Spring

Chapter
17

Lab Preview

1. Wearing safety goggles in this activity will protect your eyes from what? _____

2. What will you do with the yarn in this activity? _____

_____

You have learned about longitudinal and transverse waves. How do waves travel on a coiled spring? Are they transverse waves or longitudinal waves?

PROBLEM
How many types of waves can you create with a coiled spring?

FORM A HYPOTHESIS
As a group, decide on a hypothesis that predicts how waves can travel on a coiled spring. Write it down.

SAFETY PRECAUTIONS

OBJECTIVES
• Observe how waves travel along a coiled spring.
• Operationally define types of waves.

MATERIALS
coiled metal spring
piece of colored yarn

PLAN THE EXPERIMENT
1. Examine the materials and decide how you will test your hypothesis. Write down your plan.
2. In your Science Journal, prepare a place to draw diagrams of the wave types your group creates with the coiled spring. Plan to use arrows on the diagrams to show direction of movement.

CHECK THE PLAN
1. Determine if two people will hold the spring or you will let the spring hang down.
2. Before you begin, check your plan with your teacher.
3. Do the experiment. Make certain that you observe closely to see what kinds of waves you can make and to see what happens to the waves when they reach the end of the coil. Do they come back? Observe closely and in your Science Journal draw diagrams of what occurs.

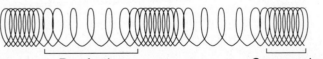

Rarefaction   Compression

Design Your Own Investigation 17-1 (continued)

ANALYZE AND CONCLUDE

1. Observe What types of wave pulses did you create? _____

_____

2. Interpret Data Draw a diagram of each type of wave that occurred in the spring. Label your

diagrams. Show direction of the movement. _____

_____

3. Did the waves move in the same direction as the source of the disturbance? Explain.

_____

_____

4. Observe What happened when the waves reached the end of the spring? _____

_____

_____

5. Infer Compare the motion of a radio speaker tested in the Find Out! activity to the waves you
created with the spring. Is a sound wave a transverse or longitudinal wave? Is an ocean wave a

transverse or longitudinal wave? _____

GOING FURTHER

Observe how fast transverse and longitudinal waves move along the spring. Can you change the

speed or is there a set speed? _____

_____

I N V E S T I G A T E !   Text Page 552   Chapter 17

17-2 Ripples

Lab Preview

1. How will you create waves in the water? _____

   _____

2. How do you shorten the wavelength in this activity? _____

   _____

Do water waves behave the same as people waves and spring waves? How are their speed, frequency, and wavelength related? In this activity you will use the patterns produced by light shining through the crests and troughs of waves in a shallow dish to investigate water waves.

PROBLEM

How are a wave's frequency and wavelength related?

MATERIALS

clear glass dish approximately 30-cm square
pencil or pen
1 piece of blank white paper
strips of plastic foam
tape
water
overhead light
ruler

SAFETY PRECAUTIONS

WHAT TO DO

1. Tape strips of plastic foam to the inner edges of the dish (see photo **A**, page 553 of your text). Then, fill the clear glass dish with about 3 cm of water (see photo **B**, page 553 of your text). Set it on a piece of blank white paper under an overhead light source.

2. Tap the water with the end of your pencil or pen. Observe the wave by looking at the paper. In the space provide below or *in your Journal,* draw the shape of the wave. Compare the speed of the wave in all directions. How fast does the wave travel? Estimate how long it takes to travel the length of the dish.

3. Now, tap the water again, producing a series of waves. Increase the frequency by tapping the water faster and observe the change in wavelength. Draw an example of low- and high-frequency waves being produced.

Investigate 17-2 (continued)

ANALYZING

1. What effect does increasing the frequency have on the wavelength of the waves produced in Step 3?

_____

_____

2. What would happen to the wavelength if you decreased the frequency? _____

_____

CONCLUDING AND APPLYING

3. What is the relationship between wavelength and frequency in water waves? _____

_____

_____

4. Going Further: Predict whether the wave speed depends on the water depth. *In your Journal* write a plan about how you could make different depths of water in the same dish and find out.

_____

_____

_____

_____

DESIGN YOUR OWN
INVESTIGATION

18-1 Locating Active Volcanoes

Chapter 18

Lab Preview

1. How will you use the tracing paper? _____

2. What will you add to the tracing to help with location? _____

_____

Volcanoes form when hot, melted rock material is forced upward to Earth's surface. As the melted rock moves inside Earth, vibrations occur, which are felt as earthquakes. How would you determine whether active volcanoes are located near earthquake epicenters?

PROBLEM

Is there a connection between the locations of active volcanoes and the locations of recent earthquakes?

FORM A HYPOTHESIS

As a group, discuss the areas where earthquakes and volcanoes are commonly located. Then

form a hypothesis about whether you expect to see a relationship between the locations of active volcanoes and the locations of earthquake epicenters.

OBJECTIVES

- Plot the locations of several active volcanoes.
- Describe patterns of distribution for volcanoes and earthquake epicenters.
- Relate the locations of active volcanoes to the locations of recent earthquakes.

MATERIALS

world map (Appendix H)
tracing paper

Volcano	Latitude	Longitude
#1	64°N	19°W
#2	28°N	34°E
#3	43°S	172°E
#4	35°N	136°E
#5	18°S	68°W
#6	25°S	114°W
#7	20°N	155°W
#8	54°N	167°W
#9	16°N	122°E
#10	28°N	17°W

Volcano	Latitude	Longitude
#11	15°N	43°E
#12	6°N	75°W
#13	64°S	158°E
#14	38°S	78°E
#15	21°S	56°E
#16	38°N	26°E
#17	7°S	13°W
#18	2°S	102°E
#19	38°N	30°W
#20	54°N	159°E

Design Your Own Investigation 18-1 (continued)

PLAN THE EXPERIMENT

1. As a group, agree upon a way to test your hypothesis. Write down what you will do at each step of your test.

2. Examine the volcano latitude and longitude chart. What is the best way to plot the data on a tracing of Earth's surface?

3. Examine the map of earthquake epicenters on page 578. How will you compare your data with this map?

CHECK THE PLAN

Discuss and decide upon the following points and write them down.

1. As a group, decide how you will summarize your data.

2. How will you determine whether certain facts or conditions indicate a correlation between the locations of active volcanoes and earthquake epicenters?

3. Make sure your teacher approves your experiment before you proceed.

4. Carry our your experiment. Record your observations.

ANALYZE AND CONCLUDE

1. Interpret Scientific Illustrations Describe any patterns of distribution formed by active

volcanoes. _____

_____

2. Interpret Scientific Illustrations Describe any patterns of distribution formed by earthquake

epicenters. _____

_____

3. Compare and Contrast How did the patterns that you observed in the distribution of volcanoes

compare with the locations of earthquake epicenters? _____

_____

GOING FURTHER

How are the locations of volcanoes and earthquake epicenters related to Earth's geographic features?

_____

_____

_____

_____

I N V E S T I G A T E !

18-2 Making a Model Seismograph

Lab Preview

1. This activity requires two people. Describe what each person will do to record seismic

   vibrations. _____

   _____

2. What portion of a wave is defined as amplitude? _____

   _____

In this activity, you will make a model seismograph and record some vibrations.

PROBLEM

How can you measure the magnitude of vibrations?

MATERIALS

ring stand with ring
wire hook from coat hanger
masking tape
sheet of paper
piece of string
2 rubber bands
fine-tip marker
metric ruler

WHAT TO DO

1. Copy the data table *into your Journal.*
2. Set up your seismograph using the illustration

on page 591 of your text as a guide.

3. Place a sheet of paper under the ring. Adjust the position of the marker so that its tip just touches near the end of the paper.
4. Work with a partner. While one person strikes the table several times with equal strength, the other one should slowly pull the paper under the marker.
5. Recall from Chapter 17 that amplitude is half the height of wave from crest to trough. *Measure* the amplitude marked on your paper. Record your measurements and observations as Trial 1.
6. *Hypothesize* about the effect of the magnitude of the vibrations on the amplitude of the peaks.
7. Repeat Steps 3 and 4, hitting the table with less strength for Trial 2 and more strength for Trial 3. Record your measurements and observations.

DATA AND OBSERVATIONS

Trial Number	Amplitude (Height of Marks)	Observations
1		
2		
3		

Investigate 18-2 (continued)

ANALYZING

1. Which trial resulted in the greatest amplitudes recorded on the wavy line? _____

2. How did the movement of the marker compare with the movement of the frame of the

   seismograph? _____

   _____

   _____

CONCLUDING AND APPLYING

3. How does your hypothesis *compare* with the results of the activity? _____

   _____

   _____

4. Determine the effect the magnitude of vibrations had on the amplitude of the wave peaks.

   _____

   _____

   _____

5. **Going Further:** What difference would you *predict* between the amplitudes generated by a strong

   earthquake and those generated by a weaker one? _____

   _____

   _____

DESIGN YOUR OWN
INVESTIGATION

19-1 Tilt and Temperature

Lab Preview

1. Why should you handle lamps carefully in experiments? _____

_____

2. What instrument will you use to determine the angle of the lamp light? _____

Earth's tilt causes the amount of sunlight that strikes Earth to vary from one hemisphere to the other, depending on the season. How might this affect the amount of heat from the sun received by an area?

PROBLEM

How is the angle at which light strikes an area related to the amount of heat energy received by that area?

FORM A HYPOTHESIS

As a group, discuss the effects of light striking an area from several different angles. At what angle would the area receive the most heat? Agree upon a hypothesis that can be tested in your experiment.

OBJECTIVES

• Use a model to measure the amount of heat received by an area from light striking the area at different angles.
• Describe how the angle at which light strikes an area is related to Earth's changing seasons.

POSSIBLE MATERIALS

black construction paper
protractor
Celsius thermometer
watch
tape
gooseneck lamp with 75-watt bulb

SAFETY

Do not touch the lamp. The lightbulb and shade can be hot even when the lamp has been turned off. Handle the thermometer carefully. If it breaks, do not touch anything. Inform your teacher immediately.

PLAN THE EXPERIMENT

1. As a group, agree upon how you will use the materials provided to test your hypothesis.
2. Write down exactly what you will do during each step of your test.
3. Make a list of any special properties you expect to observe or test.
4. Identify any constants, variables, and controls in your experiment.

DATA AND OBSERVATIONS

Temperature At	Start	____ Min.	____ Min.	____ Min.
Direct Light				
Angled Light				

Design Your Own Investigation 19-1 (continued)

CHECK THE PLAN

1. How will you determine whether the length of time the light is turned on affects heat energy?

2. How will you determine whether the angle at which light strikes an area causes changes in heat and energy?

3. Make sure your teacher approves your experiment before you proceed.

4. Carry out your experiment. Record your observations.

ANALYZE AND CONCLUDE

1. Observe Did the temperature in the envelope continue to rise at the same rate every three minutes? _____

2. Interpret Data How does the angle of light affect temperature? How might this be related to Earth's changing seasons? _____

_____

_____

_____

3. Design an Experiment Did your experiment support your hypothesis? If not, determine how you might change the experiment in order to retest your hypothesis. _____

_____

_____

GOING FURTHER

Predict how the absorption of heat would be affected by changing your independent variables. Try your experiment with different values for your independent variables. _____

_____

_____

I N V E S T I G A T E !

19-2   Eclipses and Moon Phases

Lab Preview

1. In this activity, what object represents the sun? _____

2. Why are you cautioned to observe thermal safety in this exercise? _____

_____

You know that moon phases and solar eclipses result from the relative positions of the sun, the moon, and Earth. In this activity, you will demonstrate the positions of these bodies during certain phases and eclipses. You will also see why only a very small portion of Earth sees a total solar eclipse.

PROBLEM
How can you demonstrate moon phases and solar eclipses?

MATERIALS
pencil
unshaded light source
polystyrene ball
globe

SAFETY PRECAUTIONS

Be careful, the exposed bulb will be hot.

WHAT TO DO
1. Copy the data table *into your Journal*.
2. Stick the pencil into the polystyrene ball, *making a model* moon with a handle.

3. Set the globe and the lamp on the table about 0.5 m apart and turn on the light.
4. Holding the model moon by its pencil handle, move it around the globe to duplicate the position that will cause a solar eclipse. Record your observations in the data table and *in your Journal*.
5. Use this sun-Earth-moon model to duplicate the phases of the moon. During which phase(s) of the moon could a solar eclipse occur? How can you use the model to observe the umbra and penumbra of the moon?

DATA AND OBSERVATIONS

Moon Phase	Observations
New	
First Quarter	
Full	
Third Quarter	

Investigate 19-2 (continued)

ANALYZING

1. During which phase(s) of the moon is it possible for a solar eclipse to occur? _____

_____

2. *Determine the effect* that a small change in the distance between Earth and the moon would have

on the size of the shadow during an eclipse. _____

_____

3. As seen from Earth, how does the apparent size of the moon *compare* with the apparent size of

the sun? How can an eclipse be used to confirm this? _____

_____

_____

CONCLUDING AND APPLYING

4. Why doesn't a solar eclipse occur every month? Explain your answer. _____

_____

5. Suppose you wanted to make a more accurate model of the movement of the moon around
Earth. How might you adjust the distance between the light source and the globe? How would

you adjust the size of the moon model in comparison with the globe you are using? _____

_____

6. **Going Further:** *Hypothesize* what would happen if the sun, the moon, and Earth were lined up

with Earth directly in between the sun and moon. _____

_____

I N V E S T I G A T E !
Saving the Soil

Lab Preview

1. What will you do first? _read the description of each model in Step 4 and form a hypothesis for which one will work best_

2. What five methods can be used to control soil erosion? _One pan is the control; other pans are used for mulching, other soil cover, terracing, and contour plowing._

You've seen eroded soil and you're probably aware of the problems erosion can cause. But how do you begin to explore how to solve these problems?

PROBLEM
Which of five methods is the best way to control soil erosion?

MATERIALS
5 aluminum 8- or 9-inch pie pans
leaves or grass clippings
500-mL beaker
water
metric ruler
newspaper
pebbles
potting soil
watering can
dishpan

SAFETY PRECAUTIONS

WHAT TO DO
1. Before you start, read the description of each model in Step 4 below, and decide which one you think will work best to solve the problem above. That method is your hypothesis, the answer you expect to get after you do the experiment.

2. Fill each pan almost to the rim with soil. Pat the soil until the surface is firm and flat. Soak the soil by pouring 100 mL of water into each pan.

3. Set one pan aside as the control for this experiment.

4. Use the other four pans to set up these conditions:
   a. Mulching: Cover the surface with a layer of grass clippings or leaves.
   b. Other soil cover: Tear the newspaper into small strips. Lay the strips across the surface, leaving about 5 mm between each strip.
   c. Terracing: Build two small walls of pebbles.
   d. Contour plowing: Use your finger to make a curved groove across the surface.

5. Follow this procedure with all five pans, starting with the control:
   a. Measure 200 mL of water into the watering can.
   b. Hold the pan so that one side touches the edge of the dishpan and the opposite edge is about 10 cm higher.
   c. Slowly pour the water onto the soil at the top of the pan. Wait until the excess water runs across the soil and into the dishpan. Note: Be sure to hold the terracing and contour plowing pans so the water runs across the pebble walls and the grooves.
   d. Pour the water and soil from each pie pan into the beaker. Measure it and record the results in a data table you construct in the space provided. When the soil settles to the bottom, measure and record its height in the beaker.

6. As a class, decide which method was most effective at preventing erosion.

Investigate Introduction

DATA AND OBSERVATIONS
Answers will depend on the data tables developed by the students.

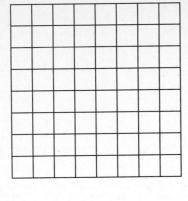

ANALYZING
1. In the space provided above, construct a graph to show results for all five pans. _Answers will vary, but contour plowing should show some of the best results._ _Students should observe that some pans should show less erosion than the control._

2. Compare and contrast the results for the pans. _methods are more effective than others. Results will vary among groups. All "treated"_

CONCLUDING AND APPLYING
3. Was your hypothesis correct? _Answers will vary depending on individual trials. However, students may say that some results were equally good and further experiments are necessary._

4. Going Further: One test or experiment isn't enough to prove a hypothesis. Most scientists perform numerous tests. Write an outline for another test of this hypothesis that does not use a model. _Accept all reasonable proposals. Possible ideas might be to observe areas of erosion and areas not eroded around the school or neighborhood. Students may propose an experiment in the school yard that could involve gardening or seeding an area in grass._

Text Page 30

Lab Preview

1. On what will you be marking the contour lines? **transparency**
2. How will you create landform contours in the box? **by pouring in water to different levels**

How can a map show the shape of a landform? In the following activity, you will show the elevations of a landform by drawing contour lines, which are lines of equal elevation that show the shape of the landform.

PROBLEM
How can elevation of a landform be indicated on a map?

MATERIALS
metric ruler
clear plastic box and lid
model landform
water
transparency marker
transparency
tape
beaker

SAFETY PRECAUTIONS

WHAT TO DO
1. Using the ruler and the transparency marker, measure and mark 2-cm lines up the side of the box.
2. Secure the transparency to the outside of the box lid with tape.
3. Place the plastic model in the box. The bottom of the box will be zero elevation.
4. Using the beaker, pour water into the box to a height of 2 cm. Place the lid on the box.
5. Looking down at the top of the box, use the transparency marker to trace the top of the water line on the transparency.
6. Using the scale 2 cm = 5 ft, mark the elevation on the line.
7. Repeat Steps 4-6, adding water to the next 2-cm level and tracing until you have mapped the landform by means of contour lines.
8. Transfer the tracing of the contours of the landform onto paper.

7

Investigate 1-1 (continued)

ANALYZING
1. What is the contour interval of this contour map? **5 ft**
2. *Interpret* the relationship between contour lines on the map and the steepness of the slope on the landform. **The closer the contour lines, the steeper the slope. Increased distances between contour lines indicate relatively flat areas.**
3. Calculate the total elevation of the landform. **Elevations will vary, but every 2 cm of the model are equal to 5 ft.**

CONCLUDING AND APPLYING
4. How are elevations shown on topographic maps? **by contour lines**
5. Explain whether all topographic maps must have a 0-ft elevation contour line. **They do not because all parts of the world aren't near sea level or 0 ft.**
6. Going Further: How would the contour interval of an area of steep mountains *compare* with the interval of an area of flat plains? **Maps with steep mountains will have a larger contour interval because the linear distance between contour lines is very small.**

8

84

DESIGN YOUR OWN INVESTIGATION

1-2 Formation of Moon Craters

Lab Preview

1. What does the flour and salt mixture represent in this activity? __the surface of the moon__

2. What will you do with the marbles and balls to simulate the formation of craters? __Drop them into the mixture from various heights.__

A crater is made when an object from space strikes the surface of Earth, the moon, or another planet, leaving a dent behind. Before you begin this investigation, make a few craters in a mixture of flour and salt as described in the Materials list. Observe what happen when you drop different "celestial objects" from different heights.

PROBLEM

What factors determine how deep a crater will be?

FORM A HYPOTHESIS

A hypothesis is a prediction or explanation that can be tested. From your observations, have your group list factors that might determine how deep a crater will be. Each group should make a hypothesis about one factor. A hypothesis might be that a heavier ball will make a deeper crater.

OBJECTIVES

• Observe what factors are important in creating a deep crater.
• Analyze your data to find what factors determine the depth of a crater.

MATERIALS

25 × 30-cm pan, one-third full of table salt and two-thirds full of flour
marbles and small balls
metric ruler
pan balance
string

SAFETY PRECAUTIONS

PLAN THE EXPERIMENT

1. Your group should test only one hypothesis. List specific steps needed to test it. Each experiment should test only one variable. A variable is the one factor that changes in each experiment, such as the size of the marbles.

2. Examine the materials provided. Decide which balls and marbles to use.

3. Design data tables in your Science Journal or on a computer word processor or database. Record information about each object before you start the test. What is it? How heavy is it? What height will it be dropped from?

CHECK THE PLAN

1. In what order will you test the variables? Does your data table match the test order?

2. Make sure your teacher approves your experiment before you proceed.

3. Carry out your experiment. Record your observations.

Design Your Own Investigation 1-2 (continued)

ANALYZE AND CONCLUDE

1. **Observe and Infer** Was your hypothesis supported by the data? Use your data to explain why or why not. __Student data should support the hypothesis.__

2. **Interpreting Data** What factors proved most important in determining how deep a crater could be? What factors did not seem to matter? __The mass (or density) of the ball and the height from which it was dropped were important factors. Color and texture of the ball were unimportant.__

3. **Draw a Conclusion** From the information in question 2, make a general statement about how to make the deepest crater. __You can make the deepest crater by dropping the heaviest (most dense) ball from the greatest height.__

GOING FURTHER

Design a similar investigation to find out what determines the diameter of a crater. __The diameter of a crater is affected by the circumference of the ball. It is also affected by mass because a big, lightweight ball will not sink far into the flour and therefore would not create a very wide crater.__

Text Page 62   Chapter 2

2-1 Mirror Reflections

Lab Preview

1. What do you use to reflect a beam of light? **mirrors and a flashlight**

2. Where do you reflect the first light beam? **onto the ceiling**

When you see light reflected from a mirror, you see an entire object—your head, a car, or a chair, for example. You probably don't think about what happens when light reflects in a mirror. You can easily discover how mirrors reflect light in this activity.

PROBLEM
How does light reflect in a mirror and how can this be used?

MATERIALS
4 pocket mirrors
flashlight
book

DATA AND OBSERVATIONS
Descriptions and Diagrams
Descriptions and diagrams will vary depending on students' results.

WHAT TO DO

1. With a partner in a darkened room, use the mirrors and the flashlight to experiment with a beam of light.

2. Using as many mirrors as necessary, first reflect a light beam onto the ceiling.

3. Now, place a book upright on a desk.

4. Position the mirrors so that a light beam striking a mirror placed in front of the book is reflected to the back of the book.

5. Now, use your mirrors to reflect light into another room.

6. Using descriptions and diagrams, record the different positions of the mirrors, the flashlight, and the light beam for each trial in the space provided below and copy them *in your Journal.*

11

Investigate 2-1 (continued)

ANALYZING

1. Make a statement that tells how light is reflected from a mirror. **Light is reflected from a mirror at the same angle which it strikes the mirror.**

2. What must you do to make the light beam change direction? **cause the beam to be reflected from a mirror**

3. If you reversed the positions of the flashlight and the point at which the reflected beam strikes an object, how would the path of the light be affected? **no change in the light's path, but direction would be opposite.**

CONCLUDING AND APPLYING

4. When might it be necessary to bounce light with mirrors? Name some situations in which a mirror would be more convenient than a light source. **Bathrooms, clothing stores, makeup counters, oldstyle signal system, telescopes, binoculars, some types of lasers. Anytime there is no straight-line path to where light is needed.**

5. *Predict* how you would arrange your flashlight and mirrors to get an image of the flashlight that would continue to be reflected from one mirror to the other. Write your prediction *in your Journal* and then try it. **Place two mirrors parallel and facing one another. Put the flashlight between them.**

6. **Going Further:** Construct a periscope to see around corners or over fences using what you have learned in this activity. Draw a diagram in the space provided below to show how the light enters the periscope and reaches the viewer's eye. **Mirrors in a periscope face each other, are parallel, and are placed at 45° to the long axis of the periscope. Light enters the periscope, is reflected down the long axis, and then reflected to the user's eye.**

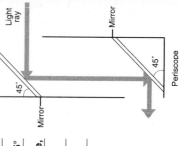

12

DESIGN YOUR OWN INVESTIGATION

2-2 Seeing Colors

Lab Preview

1. What color of paper will you use? __answers vary__

2. How many different colors will you use in this activity? __answers vary__

Think about the many things you see each day—flowers, the sky, the words and the photos on this page. Some things are easier to see than others, depending on the light, how far away from you it is, and the color.

PROBLEM

Which colors are easiest for human eyes to see? If you want the letter M to stand out from a given distance, does the color of the letter and the background affect your ability to see it?

FORM A HYPOTHESIS

Look at the photos on this page, then decide on a hypothesis predicting the easiest single color and combination of colors to see from a long distance.

OBJECTIVES

* Observe what color is easiest for most people to identify from a long distance.
* Compare and contrast color combinations for ease of identifying letters at a distance.
* Demonstrate that letters are easier to read against certain color backgrounds.

MATERIALS

scissors
glue, tape, or paper clips
posterboard and art paper of various colors including black and white

SAFETY PRECAUTIONS

Be careful when using scissors.

DATA AND OBSERVATIONS

Distance/Color			
m			
m			
m			
m			

13

Design Your Own Investigation 2-2 (continued)

PLAN THE EXPERIMENT

1. Look at the posterboard and paper. As a group decide what colors you will test for your hypothesis.

2. Discuss the best way to test your hypothesis, then write a procedure for the experiment. Make certain that colors are compared under the same conditions of distance and light.

3. Design a data table in your Science Journal or on a word processing program.

4. Determining which color or colors are easiest to identify is a judgment. Most people will agree on the easiest color to see, but perhaps not everyone. To make your data more reliable, you need to test each color more than once. Ten people determining which color is easiest to identify gives stronger information than one person determining that color.

CHECK THE PLAN

1. Make certain your data table is designed to record each individual test.

2. Before you start the experiment, have your teacher approve your plan.

3. Carry out your experiment. Make observations and record your data.

ANALYZE AND CONCLUDE

1. **Interpreting Data** Was your hypothesis supported by the data? Use your data to explain why or why not. __Students may have predicted the wrong colors, but they should be able to determine which colors were easiest to see. Research shows that yellow-green is easy to see for most people.__

2. **Using Numbers** In each experiment, add up and record the number of times a specific color was chosen as the easiest to see from a long distance away. What percentage of the time was this color chosen? Percentages are figured by dividing the number of times chosen by the total number of trials. Then multiply by one hundred and add a percent sign. Use your calculator.
__Students should use their calculators to determine percentages. They should include this figure on their data table.__

3. **Using Numbers** Find what percentage of the time the most easily seen combination of colors was chosen in the tests. __See answer #2.__

4. **Interpreting Data** Using the percentages found in the questions above, write a conclusion about which colors and color combinations are easiest to see. __This question depends on information in answer #3.__

GOING FURTHER

Inferring If you were designing a sign to be seen easily at a distance, what colors would you choose? Use your data to explain your choice. __This depends on data collected. Students may suggest yellow-green against black.__

14

DESIGN YOUR OWN INVESTIGATION

3-1 Length and Pitch

Lab Preview

1. What will you be measuring in each test tube?   the length of the air column above the
water or the amount of water and the length of the test tube

2. How many test tubes will be completely empty?   one

You have learned that shortening the length of a guitar string speeds up the vibrations and raises the pitch of the sound. If you produce a sound by blowing across a test tube full of water, what happens to the pitch of that sound when you empty the tube to half full and blow across it?

PROBLEM

When air is blown across the top of a test tube, the column of air inside the tube vibrates. When water is added to the tube, what happens? How does this added water affect pitch?

FORM A HYPOTHESIS

Based on what you have learned about changing pitch, decide on a hypothesis for your group. Write it down.

OBJECTIVES

* Observe how pitch changes with varying amounts of water in the test tube.
* Conclude from your investigation how the length of the vibrated column of air affects pitch.

MATERIALS

test tubes with an approximate diameter of 2.5 cm
test-tube rack
felt-tip marker
water
small graduated cylinder
metric ruler

SAFETY PRECAUTIONS

Be careful handling glass test tubes.

PLAN THE EXPERIMENT

1. Examine the materials and plan how your group will test the hypothesis. Write a step-by-step procedure.
2. In your Science Journal, draw diagrams of all the test tubes you use. Record your data on this diagram.
3. How will you measure the length of the column of air? Be sure to record the measurements on your diagram.

CHECK THE PLAN

1. Who will blow across the test tubes? Do the tubes need to be identical? Who will judge the sound? Do you need more than one person's opinion to judge the pitch?
2. Before you begin your experiment, make certain that your teacher approves your plan.
3. Carry out the experiment. Make observations and record your data on diagrams in your Science Journal.

Design Your Own Investigation 3-1 (continued)

ANALYZE AND CONCLUDE

1. Analyze Data Which test tube produced the lowest pitch? How much water was in it?
The one with the most water; students should record the amount of water in mL.

2. Which test tube produced the highest pitch? How much water was in it?   The one with the
least water; Students should record the amount of water in mL.

3. Compare and Contrast Compare the pitches of all the bottles. How did the amount of water in
the test tube affect the pitch of the vibrating column of air?   Adding more water to the test
tube raised the pitch.

4. Conclude Make a statement about how the length of a vibrating column of air affects its pitch.
The longer the vibrating column of air, the lower the pitch; or the shorter the vibrating
column of air, the higher the pitch.

5. Using Math From your diagram, construct a bar graph relating column size to pitch.
Students' graphs will vary but should show that as the length of the column of air
increases, the pitch decreases.

6. What basic musical instrument does your test-tube instrument resemble?   a flute

GOING FURTHER

Can you create a musical scale by blowing across test tubes with varying amounts of water in them?
How many test tubes will you need to create a musical scale of one octave?   Students will need
eight test tubes to make an octave.

3-2   Length and Resonance

Text Page 104

Lab Preview

1. How is a tuning fork's frequency measured?   in hertz

2. What do you do to the tube in this activity to discover the loudest sound?   raise and lower the test tube in the water

A tabletop resonates with the frequency of a vibrating tuning fork. The body of a guitar resonates with its vibrating strings. In this experiment, investigate the resonance of the air inside a glass tube.

PROBLEM

Can you find the length of a tube of air that will resonate with a given sound frequency?

MATERIALS

2 tuning forks of different frequencies (256 Hz or higher)
1000-mL graduated cylinder (or bucket or pitcher about 30 cm deep)
metric ruler
plastic or glass tube, 2.5 cm in diameter, about 45 cm long, open at both ends
rubber mallet
water

WHAT TO DO

1. Copy the data table *in your journal.*
2. Find the number and the letters Hz on your tuning fork and record them under *Tuning Fork Frequency* in the data table.
3. Fill the graduated cylinder or bucket with water.

4. Hold one end of the tube while you place the other end partway into the cylinder or bucket of water (see photo *A*, page 105 of your text).
5. Have your partner strike the tuning fork with the mallet and hold the fork over the tube.
6. Raise or lower the tube in the water until the loudest sound is produced.
7. Have your partner *measure* the distance from the top of the tube to the water's surface (see photo *B*, page 105 of your text). Record the length in the table. This is the length of the column of air that resonates with the vibration of the tuning fork.
8. Repeat Steps 5–7 for the second tuning fork.

DATA AND OBSERVATIONS

Sample Data

Tuning Fork Frequency	Length of the Column of Air
The higher the frequency of the tuning fork,	the shorter the length of the column of air.

Investigate 3-2 (continued)

ANALYZING

1. *Interpret* your table to answer these questions. For which tuning fork is the length of the column of air longer? Which column of air resonates at the lower frequency?   The tuning fork with the lowest frequency. The longest column.

   For which tuning fork is the lowest frequency?   The longer the tube,

2. How does the length of a column of air relate to its resonant frequency?   the lower its resonant frequency.

CONCLUDING AND APPLYING

3. Obtain a different frequency tuning fork by trading with another group. Look at its frequency and *predict* how the length of the column of air that resonates with this tuning fork will compare with your earlier trials. Record your prediction *in your journal.* Repeat the experiment and see how your prediction compares with what you observe.   Predictions should follow the rule that the greater the length of tube, the lower its resonant frequency.

4. **Going Further:** Have you ever heard an object in a room buzz when a certain note is played loudly on the radio? Explain what causes this to happen.   The musical note was the resonant frequency for that object.

4-1 Elements, Compounds, Mixtures

Text Page 124
Chapter 4

Lab Preview

1. How will you know an element? It cannot be broken down into other substances.

2. Why is it important to NOT eat foods in an experiment in the lab? Food can become contaminated.

Developing a system of classification helps turn a definition into a tool for solving problems. For example, you can classify a vehicle as a car, pick-up truck, or van based on identifying characteristics. Can a similar system be made to distinguish among elements, compounds, and mixtures?

PROBLEM

How can their differences help you distinguish among elements, compounds, and mixtures?

FORM A HYPOTHESIS

Find the definitions of elements, compounds, and mixtures from your text. If you were classifying objects based on these definitions, what characteristics would you assign to an element? To a compound? To a mixture?

OBJECTIVES

• Define *element, compound, heterogeneous mixture,* and *homogeneous mixture.*
• Develop a list of identifying characteristics based on the definitions.
• Classify an object as an element, a compound, a heterogeneous mixture, or a homogeneous mixture.

POSSIBLE MATERIALS

small amount of rock salt
glass of lemonade
aluminum foil
baking soda
small piece of granite
copper wire
piece of graphite (carbon)
vinegar and oil salad dressing

SAFETY PRECAUTIONS

Never eat, drink, or taste anything used in a laboratory experiment.

PLAN THE EXPERIMENT

1. Work as a group to choose objects and agree on a hypothesis. Record in your Science Journal the identifying characteristics that you will look for as you classify the objects.
2. Design a data table in your Science Journal to record the names of your test objects and the classifications you assign them.

CHECK THE PLAN

1. Do your identifying characteristics correspond to the definitions of substances and mixtures?
2. How will you keep track of your observations and explanations?
3. Before you begin, have the teacher check your plan and your list of objects.
4. Carry out the experiment.

19

Design Your Own Investigation 4-1 (continued)

DATA AND OBSERVATIONS

Material	Element	Compound	Mixture	
			Homogeneous	Heterogeneous
Rock salt	Results will depend on the procedures developed by the students.			
Lemonade				
Aluminum foil				
Baking soda				
Granite				
Copper wire				
Graphite				
Vinegar and oil				

ANALYZE AND CONCLUDE

1. Observe and Infer If you know the name of a substance, how can you find out if it is an element? Check to see if the name of the element is on the periodic table.

2. Compare and Contrast How do compounds differ from mixtures? The elements in a compound are chemically combined and cannot be separated by physical means. A compound has different properties from the elements that produce it.

3. Classify What homogeneous mixtures did you identify? How did you determine the difference between homogeneous and heterogeneous mixtures? Lemonade was homogeneous. Homogeneous mixtures are uniform throughout.

4. Classify Did your list of identifying characteristics help you to correctly classify the objects? How would you change your list if you were to repeat the experiment? Answers will vary.

5. Make and Use Tables Make a table that lists the four kinds of substances and mixtures, their differences, and the classifications you made. Look in the Skill Handbook under Making Tables if you need help. Check tables for correct differences and classifications of the elements, compounds, and mixtures observed.

GOING FURTHER

Use your list of identifying characteristics to classify the contents of your refrigerator at home. Identify whether there are more substances or mixtures. Students might identify pizza, salad, salsa, and soda as mixtures; baking soda and water as compounds; and aluminum (foil) as an element. Students will probably identify more mixtures than substances.

20

4-2 Using Density

Lab Preview

1. Why should you wear goggles when you are working with alcohol? __Alcohol and its__
__fumes can irritate your eyes.__

2. What mass will you measure first? __the mass of a clean, dry graduated cylinder__

In this activity, you will find the density of three materials. You will use this information to help you identify an unknown material.

PROBLEM

How can density be used to identify an unknown material?

MATERIALS

water
rubbing alcohol
unknown (liquid) substance
100-mL graduated cylinder
saturated saltwater mixture
pan balance and set of masses
goggles

SAFETY PRECAUTIONS

Avoid open flames.

WHAT TO DO

1. Copy the data table *into your Journal.*

2. Use the balance to measure the mass, in grams, of a clean, dry graduated cylinder. Record the mass in your table.

3. Fill the cylinder with water to the 50-mL mark.

4. *Measure* the mass of the filled cylinder and record it in your table under the heading *Total Mass.* Then discard the water as directed by your teacher.

5. *Calculate* the mass of the water by subtracting the mass of the empty cylinder from the total mass. Record the result under the heading *Actual Mass.*

6. Repeat Steps 3–5, first using the salt water, then the rubbing alcohol, and finally the unknown material. CAUTION: *Alcohol burns readily, and its fumes can be irritating. Wear goggles. Be sure that the room is well-ventilated, and there are no open flames.*

7. Record the data for each material.

DATA AND OBSERVATIONS

Sample Data

Material	Mass of Cylinder	Total Mass	Actual Mass	Volume	Density (g/cm³)
Water	117.59	168.31	50.72	50 mL	1.01
Salt water	117.59	176.69	59.10	50 mL	1.18
Alcohol	117.59	162.04	44.45	50 mL	0.89
Unknown	117.59	167.60	50.01	50 mL	1.00

Investigate 4-2 (continued)

ANALYZING

1. *Calculate* the density for each material by dividing its actual mass by its volume. Round to two decimal places. __water, 1.00 g/cm³; rubbing alcohol, 0.89 g/cm³; saturated salt water,__
__1.18 g/cm³__

2. Which known material had the highest density? __salt water__

CONCLUDING AND APPLYING

3. What was the unknown material? __Answers will vary depending on the unknown used.__

4. How did finding the density of the unknown material help you identify it? __The density of the__
__unknown liquid was the same as the density of one of the known liquids.__

5. **Going Further:** What other physical properties might you also look for and measure in identifying materials? __color, boiling point, melting point, odor__

I N V E S T I G A T E !

5-1 Evaporation and Solutions

Lab Preview

1. Why is it recommended to wear safety goggles in this activity? __to prevent splashing of Epsom salt solution into eyes__

2. What do you do with the string in this activity? __You place it between beakers with the ends submerged in the solutions.__

You've seen that solutions cannot be separated by letting them stand or by filtering. In this activity, you'll try to separate a solution using evaporation.

PROBLEM

Can solutions be separated by evaporation?

MATERIALS

safety goggles
Epsom salt (magnesium sulfate)
large beaker (400 mL)
thick, water-absorbent string
water
graduated cylinder (100 mL)
2 small beakers (250 mL)
spoon or stirring rod

SAFETY PRECAUTIONS

WHAT TO DO

1. Copy the data table *into your Journal.*

2. Put on your safety goggles. *Measure* 200 mL of water into a graduated cylinder and then pour this into the large beaker.

3. Dissolve as much Epsom salt as you can in the water. To do this, slowly add the solute to the water until some of the solute stays undissolved after stirring.

4. Fill the two small beakers with the Epsom-salt solution. Place them side by side about 10 cm apart. Drape the string between the beakers with the ends of the string submerged in the solutions. It should be set up as in the illustration (see photo A, page 159 of your text). The string should sag slightly between the beakers. Let the setup stand undisturbed for several days.

5. *Observe* the setup every few days and record your observations in your data table.

DATA AND OBSERVATIONS

Sample Data

Date	Observations	
	Beakers	String
	Each day, water level decreases and greater amount.	crystals build up on string in a

---

Investigate 5-1 (continued)

ANALYZING

1. What happened to the water level in the beakers? Where did the water go? __The water level went down. The water evaporated into the air.__

2. What happened on the string between the beakers? __It dripped liquid and formed a white crust hanging down from the string and building up under it.__

CONCLUDING AND APPLYING

3. *Predict* the effect of the following changes in the outcome of this Investigation.

a. You dissolved only half as much Epsom salt in the water. __There will be less crust on the string.__

b. No string was placed between the beakers. __The crust would be left in the beakers.__

4. Which part of a solid-liquid solution evaporated in the activity, the solute or the solvent? Which part was left behind? __solvent; solute__

5. *Going Further: Infer* why evaporation can't be used to separate gas-gas solutions. __A liquid turns to gas when it evaporates. In a gas-gas solution, the solvent is already gas, so further evaporation cannot occur.__

DESIGN YOUR OWN INVESTIGATION

5-2 Saturating a Solution at Different Temperatures

Lab Preview

1. Explain the meaning of the safety symbols in this activity. __Safety goggles should be worn to protect the eyes during this activity; an apron should be worn to protect clothing; and heat will be used in this activity, so students should be cautious.__

2. As you watch the sugar solution cool, how will you know when it reaches the saturation point? __Crystals will begin to form in the solution.__

A solvent can dissolve only a certain amount of solute before it is saturated. However, changing the temperature changes the situation. The point of saturation is different for different temperatures.

PROBLEM

How does the solubility of table sugar in water change at different temperatures?

FORM A HYPOTHESIS

Form a hypothesis about whether there is a change in solubility for sugar when temperature is changed. How will solubility change when temperature changes?

OBJECTIVES

- Predict how the saturation point of a solution will change with differing temperatures.
- Measure the temperature at the saturation point for different solutions.

MATERIALS

a two-hole stopper containing a thermometer
   and a copper wire stirrer
large test tube
test-tube holder
distilled water
table sugar
graduated cylinder
laboratory balance
hot plate
beaker of water
safety goggles
oven mitt

SAFETY PRECAUTIONS

Be careful when using the hot plate and when inserting the stopper into the test tube.

DATA AND OBSERVATIONS

Sample Data

Grams of Sugar	mL of Water	Saturation Temperature (°C)	Grams of Sugar Per 100 g of Water
28.7	10	60°C	287
28.7	12	40°C	239
28.7	14	20°C	205

Design Your Own Investigation 5-2 (continued)

PLAN THE EXPERIMENT

1. You will need to find the temperature at the saturation point for different solutions. The saturation point is reached when the solution cools enough that crystals of solute begin to form in the solution. If you begin with 28.7 g of sugar and 10 mL of water and run one test, how would you change the solution for another test? Would you add 2 mL of water? Would you add 2 g of sugar? In your group, decide how you will change the solution for each of three trials.

2. Copy the data table into your Science Journal and record the second and third solutions your group has agreed to test.

3. Set up the equipment as shown in the photo on page 168. How will you dissolve the sugar? You should not need to heat the solution to more than 80°C. How will you find the saturation point? Watch the temperature closely as the solution cools and you look for crystals.

CHECK THE PLAN

1. What will stay constant in the three trials? What will change?
2. Will you stir the contents of the tube while it heats? While it cools?
3. Before you start the experiment, have your teacher approve your plan.
4. Carry out your experiment. Make observations and complete your data table in your Science Journal.

ANALYZE AND CONCLUDE

1. **Use Math** Calculate the grams of sugar per 100 g of water at each saturation temperature. Use the following formula and insert the appropriate numbers for grams of sugar and milliliters of water from your data table.

$$\text{Mass of sugar} = \frac{?\text{ g sugar}}{?\text{ mL water}} \times 100 \text{ mL water}$$

Check calculations. The first answer will be 287 g of sugar at about 60°C. If they change the amount of water, the answers will be 239 g and 205 g. If they change the amount of sugar, the answers will be 307 g and 327 g. __If the amount of water is__

2. **Measure in SI** What were the three saturation temperatures? __changed, the temperatures are 60°C, 40°C, and 20°C. If the amount of sugar is changed, the temperatures are 60°C, 65°C, and 73°C.__

3. **Compare and Contrast** How did the mass of sugar that dissolved in 100 g of water change as the temperature changed? __Less sugar could dissolve at lower temperatures.__

4. **Hypothesize** Explain how your hypothesis was supported or disproved. ___Answers will vary.___

5. **Use Graphs** Graph the solubility versus temperature for the sugar-water solution.
__Graphs should approximate the curve for sucrose in Figure 5-10 on page 167.__

GOING FURTHER

Predict the solubility of sugar at 0°C, the freezing point of water, and at 100°C, the boiling point of water. __179 g, 487 g__

Chapter 6

DESIGN YOUR OWN INVESTIGATION

6-1 Identifying Acids and Bases

Lab Preview

1. What safety equipment will you use during this activity? apron and goggles
2. Predict which substances will be acidic. Answers will vary. Lemon juice, vinegar, and carbonated beverages are all acidic.

Acids and bases are used for different purposes. Their uses often correspond to the way they react to various substances. Litmus paper, which is red in the presence of an acid and blue in the presence of a base, can be used to identify acids and bases.

PROBLEM
How can acids and bases be identified?

FORM A HYPOTHESIS
As a group, form a hypothesis that will help you determine which substances are acids and which are bases.

OBJECTIVE
• Identify acids and bases based on their reactions with litmus paper.

POSSIBLE MATERIALS
test-tube rack
(6) test tubes
household ammonia
cola
table salt
lemon juice
vinegar
baking soda
orange slices
deodorant
piece of antacid tablet
red and blue litmus paper
stirring rods
distilled water

SAFETY PRECAUTIONS
Goggles and apron should be worn at all times when using these weak acids and bases. Do not allow the substances to contact your skin.

PLAN THE EXPERIMENT
1. Within your group, choose six of the available substances to test.
2. What procedure will you follow to test each substance? Will you use both kinds of litmus paper? Is it important to use clean stirring rods?
3. Water is a neutral liquid; it is neither acidic nor basic. How will you use it as you test the solids?
4. How will you keep track of your findings? In your Science Journal, design a table or chart to use during your experiment.

CHECK THE PLAN
1. Have another group read your plan after they have finished writing their own. Do they understand what you plan to do?
2. Before you begin, have your teacher approve your plan.
3. Carry out the experiment.

27

Design Your Own Investigation 6-1 (continued)

Sample Data

DATA AND OBSERVATIONS

Material tested	Effects on Litmus Paper		
	Red to Blue	Blue to Red	No Effect
Lemon juice		x	
Ammonia	x		
Distilled water			x
Vinegar		x	
Cola		x	
Baking soda	x		
Table salt			x
Orange slices		x	
Deodorant	x		
Antacid tablet	x		

ANALYZE AND CONCLUDE
1. **Observe** What changes did you observe for acids? For bases? Acids turned blue litmus red. Bases turned red litmus blue.
2. **Infer** Which substances did you infer were acids? Bases? Lemon juice, vinegar, cola, and the orange slice were acids. Ammonia, baking soda, the antacid tablet, and the deodorant were bases.
3. **Analyze** How effective was your procedure? Are there things you would change if you were to do it again? Answers will vary.
4. **Conclude** List any substances that showed no change with the litmus test. What can you determine about them? Salt and distilled water showed no color change. Both are neutral—neither acidic nor basic.

GOING FURTHER
Predict how the bases you identified in the Explore activity on page 193 would affect litmus paper. Acids would turn blue litmus red. Bases would turn red litmus blue.

28

Text Page 200 ———— Chapter **6**

6-2 Finding pH

Lab Preview

1. Why should you wear an apron during this activity? **Some of the material in this**

activity could stain or damage clothing.

2. How much cabbage juice do you use for each test tube? **15 mL**

Certain substances change color when pH changes. A common substance of this type found in nature is red cabbage juice. In this Investigate, you will test the pH of household liquids using red cabbage juice.

PROBLEM

How can cabbage juice indicate the relative pH of acids and bases?

MATERIALS

safety goggles
7 test tubes
100-mL graduated cylinder
apron
test-tube rack
red cabbage juice
grease pencil
7 dropping bottles with: household ammonia, colorless carbonated soft drink, baking soda solution, sodium hydroxide solution, hydrochloric acid solution, distilled water, white vinegar

SAFETY PRECAUTIONS

Use caution when working with acids and bases. Wear lab aprons and goggles.

WHAT TO DO

1. *In your journal*, make a data table in which you can record your prediction of pH, the color of the cabbage juice, and the relative

pH of the acid or base for each of the seven solutions to be tested.

2. Wear an apron and goggles. Mark each test tube with the substance name.

3. Fill each test tube with 15 mL of the cabbage juice.

4. Use the following table of colors to predict the relative pH of the test solutions. Record these predictions in your table.

5. Add 5 drops of each test solution to the test tube labeled with its name. **CAUTION:** *If you spill any liquids on your skin, rinse the area immediately with water. Alert your teacher if any liquid is spilled in the work area.*

6. *Observe* any color changes of the cabbage juice. In your data table, record the color and relative pH of each solution.

Cabbage Juice Color	Relative pH
bright red	strong acid
red	medium acid
reddish purple	weak acid
purple	neutral
blue green	weak base
green	medium base
yellow	strong base

Investigate 6-2 (continued)

ANALYZING

1. *Classify* which test solutions were acids and which were bases. **Acids: soft drink, hydrochloric**

acid, vinegar; bases: ammonia, baking soda, sodium hydroxide

2. Which base was weakest? **baking soda**

3. Which acid was strongest? **hydrochloric acid**

4. *Infer* why distilled water didn't change the color of the cabbage juice. **Water is neutral.**

CONCLUDING AND APPLYING

5. How do your predictions *compare* with the results? **Answers will vary.**

6. How does cabbage juice indicate the relative strength of acids and bases? **The more yellow**

the cabbage juice turns, the more basic the substance being tested is; the brighter red

the cabbage juice turns, the more acidic the substances being tested is.

7. **Going Further:** *Predict* how other substances at home would react with the cabbage juice. Ask an

adult to help you test your predictions. **Answers will vary.**

Text Page 222

Chapter 7

7-1 Living or Nonliving?

Lab Preview

1. In this activity, what is the food? **sugar**

2. Why do you need a microscope in this activity? **Because most of the changes are impossible to see without it.**

In this section, you have learned about the traits of living things. During this investigation, you will observe how substances react to food. Use your knowledge about living things to help you prove which substances are living.

PROBLEM

How can you prove that something is living or nonliving?

FORM A HYPOTHESIS

As a group, decide on a statement or prediction about whether yeast, baking soda, and salt are living or not. Record your hypothesis.

OBJECTIVES

• Observe the changes over time when something is fed.
• Compare the reactions of test items to the traits of living organisms.

POSSIBLE MATERIALS

microscope
coverslips
1 package dry yeast
salt (NaCl)
baking soda (NaHCO$_3$)
measuring spoons
labels
4 test tubes each with 20 drops of sugar water

SAFETY PRECAUTIONS

Dispose of the yeast as directed by your teacher.

PLAN THE EXPERIMENT

1. As a group, decide how you will test your hypothesis. Design the experiment to prove if any of the three test items are alive. Write down the steps of your experiment.
2. What are the variables? What is the control? Before you begin, label the tubes for your experiment and record what each one will contain. Make certain that you use the same amount of each substance in the tests. In this experiment, sugar water is the food.
3. Make a data table. In the table, list the traits of living things that you will observe.
4. Immediately after you put each test item into the sugar water, observe a sample of each under the microscope. At the end of the experiment, observe the samples again and compare.

CHECK THE PLAN

1. Investigations like this one take time. Plan to take observations every 10 minutes for 40 minutes. After every observation, record what you saw.
2. Before you start your experiment, make certain your teacher approves your plan.
3. Carry out the experiment.

Design Your Own Investigation 7-1 (continued)

Sample Data

DATA AND OBSERVATIONS

Time	A	B	C	D
After ___ minutes	At first, there will be no change in most.			
After ___ minutes				
After ___ minutes	Bubbles should appear in the yeast.			
After ___ minutes				

ANALYZE AND CONCLUDE

1. **Observe** How did test tubes A, B, C, and D change over the time you observed them? **The test tube with the yeast bubbled up as the yeast fed on the sugar. The other substances did not react.**

2. **Infer** What was in the test tubes that changed? Was the change an indication of a life process occurring? **Yeast; the change showed that yeast was feeding on sugar. This was an indication of digesting food, a life process.**

3. **Conclude** What waste product was produced in the experiment? What do you think it is? Why did it occur? **A gas bubbled up. Carbon dioxide was produced by the breakdown of food.**

4. **Scientific Illustration** Make drawings of what you see under the microscope at the beginning and at the end of the experiment for each tube. **Students should draw what they see in each tube at the beginning and at the end of the experiment. They should see the yeast cells.**

5. **Collect Data** In your data table, check off each trait that applies to each item tested. **Traits mentioned: organisms are made up of cells; use water and food and produce wastes; reproduce, grow, respond; and are adapted to their environment. Yeast broke down food and produced waste, had cell structure, and grew. The salt and baking soda should not have shown any of these living traits.**

6. **Conclude** Use your data to conclude whether each test item is living or nonliving. **The hypothesis that predicted that yeast is alive was supported because yeast showed traits of living things while the other substances did not.**

GOING FURTHER

Design an experiment in which you test for each of the characteristics of life as described on pages 220 and 221. **Check student designs for correct use of variables and scientific methods.**

7-2 Using a Key

Lab Preview

1. What is a key? __a step-by-step guide for identifying organisms that requires that you make a choice between two statements at each step until a name is reached for an organism__

2. How many species of jays could you identify with this key? __eight__

In this activity, you will learn to use a key to identify jay birds. A key is a step-by-step guide for identifying organisms that requires that you make a choice between two statements at each step until a name is reached for an organism.

PROBLEM
How is a key used to identify jays?

MATERIALS
paper and pencil

WHAT TO DO
1. Look at the two jays pictured on page 237 of your text.
2. Begin with Step 1 of the Key to Jays of North America. Select one statement that is true about that bird and follow the direction it takes you. Follow each succeeding step until you identify the bird by its scientific names. Use the key to classify the bird labeled **A**, on page 237 of your text.
3. Use the data table below to record the common and scientific names for the jay.
4. Now use the same procedure to classify the species of jay labeled **B**, on page 237 of your text.

KEY TO JAYS OF NORTH AMERICA
1a If the jay has a crest on the head, go to Step 2.
1b If the jay has no crest, go to Step 3.
2a If the jay's crest and upper body are mostly blue, it is a blue jay, *Cyanocitta cristata.*
2b If the jay's crest and upper body are brown or gray, it is a stellar's jay, *Cyanocitta stelleri.*
3a If the jay is mostly blue, go to Step 4.
3b If the jay has little or no blue, go to Step 6.
4a If the jay has a white throat, outlined in blue, it is a scrub jay, *Aphelocoma coerulescens.*
4b If the throat is not white, go to Step 5.
5a If the jay has a dark eye mask and gray breast, it is a gray-breasted jay, *Aphelocoma ultramarinus.*
5b If the jay has no eye mask and has a gray breast, it is a pinyon jay, *Gymnorhinus cyanocephalus.*
6a If the jay is mostly gray and has black and white head markings, it is a gray jay, *Perisoreus canadensis.*
6b If the jay is not gray, go to Step 7.
7a If the jay has a brilliant green body with some blue on the head, it is a green jay, *Cyanocorax yncas.*
7b If the jay has a plain brown body, it is a brown jay, *Cyanocorax moria.*

DATA AND OBSERVATIONS

Sample Data

Jay	Scientific Name	Common Name
A	Cyanocitta cristata	Blue jay
B	Cyanocorax yncas	Green jay

33

Investigate 7-2 (continued)

ANALYZING
1. Using the key, how many species of jay can you infer are in North America? __eight__
2. How many genera can be identified with this key? __five__

CONCLUDING AND APPLYING
3. How do you know that this key doesn't contain all the species of jays in the world? __The title of the key specifies that it is a key to jays of North America.__

4. Why wouldn't you be successful in identifying a robin using this key? __The key identifies jays not robins.__

5. Going Further: Why wouldn't it be a good idea to begin in the middle of a key, instead of with the first step? __The first pair of descriptions are the most general. The following descriptions become more specific. Correct identification depends on making the correct choice between the first pair of descriptions.__

34

8-1 Shapes of Viruses

Text Page 252

Lab Preview

1. How many models of viruses will you make in this activity? __two__

2. What does the first safety symbol mean? __Be careful not to cut yourself when working with wires.__

Viruses all contain similar structures and materials, yet they differ greatly in shape. In this activity, you can observe and make models of some viruses.

PROBLEM

How can you make a model of a virus?

MATERIALS

3.7 cm × 0.7 cm bolt
2 pieces #22-gauge wire, 14 cm long
pipe cleaners, cut in 2-cm lengths
2 nuts to fit bolt
polystyrene ball, 4.5 cm in diameter

SAFETY PRECAUTIONS

Be careful when working with wires.

WHAT TO DO

1. Look at the photographs of the viruses taken with an electron microscope on page 251 of your text. Then, study the drawings of the viruses in Figures A and B shown below. The drawing in Figure A represents a virus enlarged 260 000 times. The drawing in Figure B represents a flu virus enlarged 300 000 times.

2. Notice the parts in Figure A that are labeled. To make a model of the virus, attach two nuts onto a bolt and screw them on as far as you can.

3. Twist the wires around the bolt near the bottom. Make the wire as tight as you can. Fold the wire ends and bend them so that they look similar to the drawing.

4. Use the polystyrene ball and pipe cleaners to make a model of the flu virus in Figure B.

Head

Tail

A

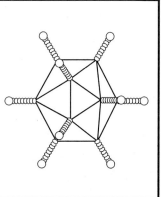

B

Investigate 8-1 (continued)

ANALYZING

1. *Compare* your models with Figures *A* and *B*. How are they alike? __Model A seems to have a head, neck, and tail with appendagelike fibers. Model B is spherelike with spikes coming from it but no other parts.__

2. *Contrast* the two viruses. How are they different from each other? __They differ in shape: A has a head, neck, and tail with appendages; B has only a head.__

3. What is there about the structure of a virus that seems to help it get inside your cells? __Students may say that a virus enters a person's cells by using its shape to attach to the cell membrane.__

CONCLUDING AND APPLYING

4. How does a virus differ from a cell? __Cells have cytoplasm, cell membranes, and other structures; a virus has only DNA or RNA with a coat around it.__

5. *Going Further:* What kinds of illnesses have you heard of that are caused by viruses? *Make a table* of at least three diseases caused by viruses that you have researched in library references. In the table, list the disease, what it affects, and where it is found. You may want to use a computer to make your table. __Answers may include flu, AIDS, colds, and chicken pox. Table should have four rows—one for heads (Disease, What It Affects, Where Found) and three for the three diseases. There should be three columns—one for each head. Students should give their tables titles. Most will choose something similar to Viral Diseases.__

8-2 The Work of Fungi

Lab Preview
1. What are the tiny threadlike branches of a mold called? __hyphae__
2. What foods will you use in your experiment? __peaches, apples, or oranges__

Have you ever seen mold grow on fruit? When conditions are right, mold can cover and penetrate a fruit with hundreds of thousands of tiny threadlike branches called hyphae. The cells of hyphae release substances that break down organic materials in the fruit. Then bacteria move in, causing spoilage.

PROBLEM
Under what conditions does a mold grow best on fruit?

FORM A HYPOTHESIS
Has anyone in your group ever seen mold on fruit? As a group, discuss the conditions under which the mold grew. Then form a hypothesis that can be tested in your experiment.

OBJECTIVES
• Design an experiment using several variables to promote mold formation on fruit.
• Compare and contrast conditions that promote mold formation.
• Infer how certain conditions interact to promote or prevent the growth of mold.

POSSIBLE MATERIALS
peaches, apples, or oranges
paper towels
plastic bags
kitchen knife or fork
paper plate
water

SAFETY PRECAUTIONS

Be careful with knives if you decide to cut any fruit. Dispose of all moldy products as directed by your teacher.

PLAN THE EXPERIMENT
1. Examine the materials provided. Decide how you will use them in your experiment.
2. Design a procedure to test your hypothesis. Write down what you will do at each step.
3. How will you record your data? If you need a table, design one now in your Science Journal.

CHECK THE PLAN
1. List the conditions that you think will promote mold formation on fruit. Which condition will you test?
2. If you are testing more than one condition, have you allowed for a control in your experiment? What is the control?
3. Make sure your teacher approves your experiment before you proceed.
4. Carry out your experiment. Record your observations.

DATA AND OBSERVATIONS
Answers will vary depending on students' experiments and tables.

Design Your Own Investigation 8-2 (continued)

ANALYZE AND CONCLUDE
1. **Compare and Contrast** Which conditions promoted mold formation? __Damp, warm, dark conditions promoted mold. Mold may also have been prevented by certain wrapping materials.__ Which conditions prevented mold formation? __Dry, cool, light conditions prevented mold.__

2. **Recognize Cause and Effect** Was your hypothesis supported? If not, explain why it might still be right. __A hypothesis might not be supported yet still may not be wrong. Further data must be collected before the hypothesis can be evaluated. For example, a student who hypothesizes that dark conditions promote mold may not see any growth if the fruits are very dry. Additional data using less dry fruits in dark and bright conditions would need to be collected before deciding whether or not darkness promotes mold.__

3. **Observe and Infer** On which fruits did mold grow the easiest? Suggest reasons for this. __The soft-skinned fruits, such as peaches, seemed to mold more easily than hard-skinned fruits, such as apples. Students may observe that mold grows more easily on fruits that are damaged.__

4. **Infer** Suggest a good use for the moldy fruit at the end of this experiment instead of throwing it into the trash. Give a reason for your suggestion. __Moldy fruit can be added to a composting bin where the molds in the fruit will help to break down other organic matter.__

5. **Interpret Data** Based on the outcome of your experiment, what steps would you take to prevent oranges from molding quickly at home? __Answers will vary but should include suggestions on keeping the oranges cool and dry.__

GOING FURTHER
You may have formed several hypotheses while designing this experiment. Test one of these hypotheses or design a new experiment based on an observation made while conducting this one. Students may wish to design experiments that will test the effects of temperature, light, humidity, acidity, or other factors on mold growth.

DESIGN YOUR OWN
INVESTIGATION

9-1 Picky Eaters

Lab Preview

1. What kinds of food will you feed to the mealworms in this activity? __bran flakes, dry oatmeal, sugar-coated corn flakes, and wheat crackers__

2. How many times will you test the response of mealworms to different foods? __several times__

Are there certain foods that you do not like to eat? Maybe you don't like spinach because of its taste or texture. Other members of your family may not like corn. Do animals, like people, have food preferences? In the following activity, you will observe how mealworms respond to different kinds of food.

PROBLEM
How can you determine the food preferences of mealworms?

FORM A HYPOTHESIS
As a group, discuss the factors that might influence the mealworms' preference for one food over another, such as moistness or odor. Agree upon these factors, then form a hypothesis about the food that mealworms prefer.

OBJECTIVES
• Design an experiment that tests the mealworms' responses to various types of foods.

• Compare the mealworms' responses to different foods.
• Infer why mealworms prefer some foods over others.

POSSIBLE MATERIALS
20 mealworms
plastic storage box
pan balance
cheesecloth
20 g bran flakes
20 g dry oatmeal
20 g sugar-coated corn flakes
20 g broken, unsalted wheat crackers

gram masses
hand lens
forceps
water

SAFETY PRECAUTIONS

Return all mealworms to your teacher at the end of the experiment. Dispose of the cereals as directed by your teacher.

DATA AND OBSERVATIONS

Sample Data

Test Food	Day 1	Day 2	Day 3	Day 4
Oatmeal	7	4	8	5
Corn Flakes		Responses of mealworms will vary.		
Wheat Crackers				
Bran Flakes				

Design Your Own Investigation 9-1 (continued)

PLAN THE EXPERIMENT
1. Examine the materials. Which materials will you use? How will you use them?
2. Agree upon a way to test your hypothesis. Write down what you will do at each step.
3. Assign tasks to members of the group.
4. Design a table for recording your data. Decide when data will be measured and recorded.
5. Decide where to place the mealworms in the box. Be sure to discuss how to move the mealworms back to their starting place so that the experiment can be repeated several times.
6. Before you start the experiment, have your teacher approve your plan.
7. Carry out your experiment. Complete your data table in your Science Journal.

CHECK THE PLAN
1. Determine where you will put the different foods in the plastic box. How will you calculate how much food the mealworms have eaten?

ANALYZE AND CONCLUDE
1. Use Numbers Calculate the total number of mealworms that preferred each food.
   __Answers will vary.__

2. Use Numbers Calculate the mealworms' daily average of food intake for each food type.
   __Answers will vary.__

3. Which type of food did most mealworms prefer? Did this support your hypothesis? Explain. __The food most mealworms preferred was cooked or moistened oatmeal. Answers will depend on students' hypotheses. Help students to understand that an unsupported hypothesis does not make it wrong. There are no right or wrong hypotheses, only supported or unsupported ones.__

4. Infer why the mealworms were attracted to a particular food. __The moist food was more easily detected by the worms.__

GOING FURTHER
Predict whether mealworms might be attracted to other food choices. Design an experiment to test this prediction. Test the prediction. __Answers will vary, but are likely to include other forms of cereals and crackers.__

9-2 Earthworm Behavior

Lab Preview

1. How should you handle the worms during this experiment? **They should be held gently and kept moist.**

2. Ideal conditions for an earthworm include moist earth. How might a worm react if there is too much water? **The worm would probably crawl to the surface to avoid drowning. Worms often do this during a heavy rain.**

How can you determine the effect some conditions have on an earthworm? In this activity, you will observe some earthworm characteristics and infer how they enable the earthworms to survive.

PROBLEM

How is an earthworm adapted to live in soil?

MATERIALS

hand lens
vinegar
live earthworms in slightly moist soil
500 mL beaker
toothpick
flashlight
shallow pan
paper towels
cotton swab
water

SAFETY PRECAUTIONS

Earthworms can be released into the soil then you have completed your investigation. Earthworms are valuable because they aerate and mix soil as they move through it.

WHAT TO DO

1. Copy the data table *into your Journal.*
2. Open the container to be sure some of the earthworms are on the top of the soil. Shine the flashlight on the worms. Record how the worms react.
3. Moisten your hands and remove an earthworm from the container. CAUTION: *Use care when working with live animals.* Keep your hands moist while working with the earthworm. Hold the worm gently between your thumb and forefinger. Observe its movements and record them in the table.
4. Rub your fingers gently along the body. With a hand lens, *observe* the small hair-like bristles that you feel.
5. With the toothpick, gently touch the worm on the front and back ends. Record your observations.
6. Dip the cotton swab in vinegar. Place it in front of the worm on a wet paper towel. *Do not touch the worm with the vinegar.* Record what you observe.

DATA AND OBSERVATIONS

Sample Data

Condition	Response
Light	Responses may
Fingers	vary with the
Touch-front	health of the
Touch-back	worms.
Vinegar	

Investigate 9-2 (continued)

ANALYZING

1. What happens when light is shined on the earthworms? **They move away, under the soil.**

2. How does the earthworm react to touch? **It moves away and tries to get free.**

3. How does the earthworm react to the vinegar? **It avoids the vinegar.**

CONCLUDING AND APPLYING

4. *Infer* how the earthworm's reaction to light is an adaptation for living in soil. **Its reaction provides an opportunity for the worm to stay buried in the soil where it won't dry out. It also allows it to hide or escape predators.**

5. How are the bristles an adaptations for living in soil? **The bristles provide traction, which is helpful as the worm moves in the soil.**

6. Going Further: *Design an experiment* to find out how the earthworm reacts to different temperatures. **Answers will vary. The container with worms could be placed in a larger bowl with ice cubes on one side of the worm container. Above all, the animal should be protected from harmful substances.**

Chapter

10

10-1 They're All Wet

Lab Preview

1. What three seeds will you be working with in this activity? **radish, watermelon, and bean seeds**

2. Where will you put the sprouting seeds? **between two moist paper towels**

You know that seed coats protect seeds, but a plant embryo cannot grow until this coat breaks open. In this activity, you will soak seeds in water to observe what effect this has on the seeds' coats. You will also observe whether soaking the seeds affects the time it takes them to sprout.

PROBLEM

How does soaking affect the time it takes seeds to sprout?

FORM A HYPOTHESIS

As a group, form a hypothesis about what might happen to seeds that are soaked in water for various lengths of time.

OBJECTIVES

- Predict the effect soaking has on the time it takes seeds to sprout.
- Infer what function water plays in the seeds' ability to sprout.

MATERIALS

6 small cups (paper or plastic)
12 radish seeds
12 watermelon seeds
12 bean seeds
paper towels

PLAN THE EXPERIMENT

1. Examine the materials provided by your teacher. Then design an experiment that uses these materials to test the effects of different soaking times on seeds.

2. Plan a data table in your Science Journal for recording your observations.

3. Because your test may last several weeks, assign daily tasks to all members of the group. Who will observe the seeds each day? Who will record the observations?

CHECK THE PLAN

Discuss and decide upon the following points and write them down.

1. Have you allowed for a control in your experiment? What is it?

2. How long will you conduct your test? How will you observe the sprouting seeds without injuring the seeds?

3. Make sure your teacher approves your experiment before you proceed.

4. Carry out your experiment. Record your observations.

DATA AND OBSERVATIONS

Answers will depend on the experiments developed by the students.

Design Your Own Investigation 10-1 (continued)

ANALYZE AND CONCLUDE

1. Compare and Contrast Which seeds sprouted first? Last? **The seeds that were soaked for the longest time began to grow first. If students used unsoaked seeds as a control, these seeds would sprout last.**

2. Infer What can you infer about the types of seeds and the times it took for them to sprout? **Students will observe that the different types of seeds have different seed coats, which affects the time it takes for the seeds to sprout.**

3. Separate and Control Variables Why did you soak the seeds for different amounts of time? **The seeds were soaked for different amounts of time to see whether the length of soaking time affected when a seed would begin to grow.**

4. Interpret Data Infer what function water played in this experiment. **Water was absorbed by seed tissues, which swelled and broke the seed coat.**

5. Draw a Conclusion How does soaking time affect the time it takes for a seed to begin growing? **Soaking seeds reduces germination time.** Did your observations support your hypothesis? **Answers will vary depending on hypotheses.**

GOING FURTHER

Predict what would happen if you used tea or lemon juice as a soaking solution. **Both tea and lemon juice are acids. They might weaken the seed coats faster than water.**

10-2 Stomata

Lab Preview

1. What transparent outer tissue will you be removing from the lettuce leaf? __the epidermis__

2. You will be observing how lettuce reacts to what two liquids? __water and salt solution__

You learned that stomata are openings through which oxygen, carbon dioxide, and water pass. In this activity, you will learn what stomata look like and how they work.

PROBLEM
How do stomata work?

MATERIALS
lettuce
water
microscope
salt solution
paper towel
dish
coverslip
microscope slide
forceps
pencil

SAFETY PRECAUTIONS
Use care handling the microscope.

WHAT TO DO

1. Copy the data table *into your Journal.*
2. From a dish of water containing lettuce leaves, choose a lettuce leaf that is stiff from absorbing the water.
3. Bend the leaf back and use the forceps to strip off some of the transparent tissue covering the leaf. This is the epidermis (see photo *A*, page 335 of your text).
4. Prepare a wet mount of a small section of this tissue (see photo *B*, page 335 of your text). Draw and label the leaf section in your data table.
5. Examine the specimen under low and then high power of the microscope (see photo *C*, page 335 of your text). Draw and label the leaf section in your data table.
6. *Observe* the location and spacing of the stomata. Count how many of the stomata are open.
7. Place a paper towel at the edge of the coverslip and draw out the water. Using a dropper, add a few drops of salt solution at the edge of the coverslip. The salt solution will spread out beneath the coverslip.
8. Examine the preparation under low and then high power of the microscope. Draw and label the leaf section in your data table.
9. Repeat step 6.

DATA AND OBSERVATIONS

Sample Data

	Water Mount	Salt Solution
Number of stomata	Number of stomata will vary.	
Spacing of stomata	Spacing will vary	
Drawing of leaf section	Stomata open	Stomata closed

45

Investigate 10-2 (continued)

ANALYZING

1. *Describe* the guard cells around a stoma. __Guard cells look almost like thick lips.__

2. How many stomata did you see in each leaf preparation? __The number of stomata should be about the same.__

3. *Calculate* the percentage of the stomata open in water and in salt water. Which type of water had a higher percentage of open stomata? Which had a lower percentage of open stomata? __The number of stomata present in the water mount would be approximately 12, in the salt solution approximately 10. The number of stomata open in the water mount could be approximately 10, in the salt solution approximately 2. In the water mount most stomata should be open. In the salt solution all stomata should be closed.__

CONCLUDING AND APPLYING

4. *Infer* why the lettuce leaf became stiff in water. __Tissues in the leaf absorbed water. Water diffused from guard cells to__

5. *Infer* why more stomata were closed in the salt solution. __salt solution. They lost water, so they closed.__

6. Going Further: *Predict* what would happen if you soaked the lettuce in a stronger salt solution. Would more or fewer stomata close? __More concentrated salt solutions may cause more stomata to close.__

46

11-1 What Do Owls Eat?

Text Page 354 ___ Chapter **11**

Lab Preview

1. What will you do first? ___ Answers will vary depending on the plans students develop.

2. What does the second safety symbol mean? ___ that there is danger involving bacteria, fungi, or protists

Owl pellets are made of the things an owl has swallowed, including fur and bones, that the owl is unable to digest. These pellets form in an owl's stomach and then the owl coughs them up. Examining an owl pellet can tell you much about what is going on in a small part of the owl's ecosystem.

PROBLEM
What role do owls play in their ecosystem?

MATERIALS
water
forceps
coverslip
magnifying glass
cardboard
bowl
glass slide
light microscope
owl pellet
glue

SAFETY PRECAUTIONS

Use care when handling microscope slides and coverslips. Dispose of all materials properly.

WHAT TO DO

1. With your group design a way to investigate what an owl pellet is made of and what its contents are. You should make a display of the contents of the owl pellet. After your plan has been approved by your teacher, carry it out.

2. *In your Journal*, write a short summary of your design and of what you found the contents of the owl pellet to be. Use the drawings on this page to help you identify the contents of the owl pellet.

Owl Pellet Contents

Leg bone	Rib	Mammal skull	Bird skull	Mammal Jawbone

DATA AND OBSERVATIONS
List or sketch contents of the owl pellet.
Lists, sketches, and numbers found will vary depending on the individual owl pellets.

47

Investigate 11-1 (continued)

ANALYZING

1. What made up the outside of the owl pellet? ___ Feathers and/or fur from the animals that have been eaten by the owl may make up the exterior of the pellet.

2. What did you see inside the pellet? How many of each kind of thing were there? ___ Bones; the number of bones observed will vary with each pellet.

3. What role does an owl play in its ecosystem? Is it a producer or a consumer? How do you know? It is a predator, a consumer. You can find the remains of what it consumed in the pellet.

4. Describe the niche of an owl. Include where the owl lives, when it feeds, and what it eats. ___ An owl is usually a night-hunting predator that lives in a nest in trees or other structures. The prey is often small, herbivorous mammals that live in or on the ground. The prey may be other birds or, in some cases, lizards. The niches are almost completely different except that the habitat overlaps.

Describe the niche of an owl's prey. How are the two similar? How do they differ?

CONCLUDING AND APPLYING

5. If one owl pellet is produced each day, *estimate* the number of organisms eaten by the owl in a single day. Estimate the number of organisms an owl needs to eat to survive for one year. Answers will vary depending on the number of skulls or other unique bones found. There may be as many as 5–6 skulls in a pellet. That would indicate 5–6 animals per day, resulting in the consumption of nearly 1800 prey animals per year.

6. Going Further: *Design an experiment* to figure out what might happen to the population of owls if there were a sudden population explosion in mice. ___ Answers will vary, but should include looking for signs of an increase in the owl population.

48

DESIGN YOUR OWN
INVESTIGATION

11-2 How Do Molds Grow?

Lab Preview

1. How many foods will you use? __three or four__
2. How will you add the mold to the food? __with a moist cotton swab__

Molds are fungi that can feed on just about anything. Think about where molds grow in our environment. Do they grow everywhere or are there factors that limit the growth of molds?

PROBLEM
What basic factor limits the growth of molds?

FORM A HYPOTHESIS
As a group, make a hypothesis about what factor seems most important in encouraging the growth of mold.

OBJECTIVES
- Identify factors that encourage growth of mold.
- Evaluate data.
- Determine which factor is a strong limiting factor to the growth of mold.

POSSIBLE MATERIALS
6 small paper cups
hand lens
labels
mold source
(teacher supplies)
spray bottle of water
plastic wrap

cotton swabs
dry potato flakes
dry macaroni
sugarless, dry cereal
other dry saltless,
sugarless food

SAFETY PRECAUTIONS

After transferring the mold source, wash your hands thoroughly. All surfaces in the experiment in touch with microorganisms should also be washed thoroughly. Do not inhale, taste, or touch material from the mold source. If you have a mold allergy, do not handle the mold.

PLAN THE EXPERIMENT

1. Examine the materials provided and decide how you will use them to test the group's hypothesis.
2. What is the limiting factor that you are testing? How will it be introduced in the experiment?
3. A small amount of food at the bottom of each cup is enough to feed mold. To introduce mold into each cup, rub a moist cotton swab across the dish of growing mold, then rub the cotton swab across the surface of the food in each cup. Try to put the same amount in each cup.
4. Mold grows over a period of days. Checking mold growth day by day should be taken into account in making your plan and your data table.

A

B

49

Design Your Own Investigation 11-2 (continued)

DATA AND OBSERVATIONS

Sample Data

Cup Contents	Day 1	Day 2	Day 3	Day 4
A				
B				
C	Students' observations will vary.			
D	Students should see molds growing			
E	on the wet foods by day 4.			
F				
G				
H				

CHECK THE PLAN

1. How will you keep the environment in your experimental cups from change or contamination?
2. Where will you keep your experiment? Is it a neutral environment? Are the conditions for all the cups the same?
3. How long do you think it will take the mold to grow? How often will you check the experiment? Make certain that each observation is recorded in your data table.
4. Before your begin the experiment, have it approved by your teacher.
5. Carry out your experiment and record your data.

ANALYZE AND CONCLUDE

1. **Compare and Contrast** In which cups did you see evidence of mold growth? In which cups was there no mold growth? __wet food; dry food__
2. **Infer** Determine whether there is a factor that limits the growth of mold. __water or moisture__
3. **Interpret Data** Did mold grow faster on one particular food? __Potato flakes offer a strong medium for mold growth.__
4. **Draw a Conclusion** If you wanted to package food to sell, what is one way you could prevent mold from spoiling your product? __Remove all the water from the food that you are packaging. The removal of water should inhibit mold growth.__

GOING FURTHER

Moisture is a limiting factor in mold growth. What other factors can you test to see if they limit mold growth? __If the food is moist, further factors include temperature, preservatives in food, or lack of air.__

50

DESIGN YOUR OWN
INVESTIGATION

12-1 Average Walking Speed

Lab Preview

1. Where will you conduct your walking tests? **Answers will vary.**

2. What will you use to time each test? **a stopwatch**

When you walk, do you feel more comfortable walking barefoot, in sandals, or in athletic shoes designed for walking or running? Have you ever wondered what your average speed is when you walk?

PROBLEM
Can the type of foot gear you wear increase your average walking speed?

FORM A HYPOTHESIS
As a group, form a hypothesis predicting what foot gear will increase average walking speed for each individual in your group.

OBJECTIVES
- Measure speed and find averages for each individual.
- Compare foot gear for walking speed.
- Graph and interpret your data.

MATERIALS
meterstick
masking tape
stopwatch
shoes, boots, and sandals

PLAN THE EXPERIMENT
1. This is a group activity. Each group should test its hypothesis by designing a test procedure. Write it out step by step.

2. Speed is measured in meters per second (m/s). To find average speed, you need to know the distance traveled and the length of time each individual walked.

3. A walkway of a definite size is needed to conduct tests of the hypotheses. How long will your test track be?

4. How many trials will you conduct for each individual wearing a particular type of shoe? Testing someone 5 times is more reliable than testing once.

5. What foot gear will each individual wear? Should all the individuals tested by one group wear similar foot gear? Make certain that shoes, boots, and sandals are free from mud and dirt.

6. Design data tables in your Science Journal or on a spreadsheet for recording your data.

CHECK THE PLAN
1. What is your control in this test?
2. What are your variables?
3. Who will collect the data?
4. Make certain your teacher approves your plan before you proceed.
5. Carry out the experiment, make observations, and record the data.

DATA AND OBSERVATIONS
Results will vary depending on the students' observations.

Design Your Own Investigation 12-1 (continued)

ANALYZE AND CONCLUDE

1. **Analyze** Was your hypothesis supported by the data? Use your data to explain why or why not. **Answers may vary, but students should find that running and walking shoes provide the highest average walking speeds. Students should indicate the number of individuals in their group that had the fastest average walking speed in walking or running shoes or whatever foot gear worked best for them.**

2. **Interpret** What foot gear produced the fastest average speeds in your group? **See # 1.**

3. **Analyze** Use all the class data to make bar graphs of individual speeds in each type of foot gear. This can be done on a spreadsheet. When you have a graph for each type of foot gear, analyze each one to find out who was the fastest walker in all the different shoes. Was there a foot gear that caused some individual to walk slower while others walked faster? **Make graphs of the average speeds for all the class. Sandals should have a separate bar on each graph of a foot gear he or she wore, and so on. Each individual should have a separate bar on each graph of a foot gear he or she wore.**

4. **Infer** What would happen to your average walking speed if your running shoes had wet mud on them or they were worn down? **Worn down or muddy running shoes do not provide the friction force that clean, new running shoes do. Therefore old or muddy shoes make you go slower.**

GOING FURTHER
If you have a suitable track, test which brand of running shoe increases average speed the most. **This is a good experiment for nice weather. Remember that shoes should be of approximately equal age and cleanness.**

12-2 Instantaneous Acceleration

Lab Preview

1. What part of the accelerometer will you be observing to measure instantaneous acceleration? **the string and button**

2. What data will you record from the protractor? **the angle of the string**

Have you ever wondered how quickly you can accelerate? You can make an accelerometer that will allow you to measure the instantaneous acceleration of moving objects.

PROBLEM
How can you measure instantaneous acceleration?

MATERIALS
protractor
10 to 12 cm length of string
heavy button

Conversion Chart

Moving Object	Acceleration m/s/s
90°	0
80°	1.7
70°	3.6
60°	5.7
50°	8.2
45°	9.8
40°	12
30°	17
20°	27
10°	56
0°	—

WHAT TO DO

1. Copy the data table *into your Journal.*

2. Assemble the materials as shown in the picture on page 399 of your text.

3. Hold the protractor upside down. The string should line up with the 90-degree mark on the protractor. When taking a reading, hold the protractor level.

4. Hold the accelerator at arm's length in front of your face with the numbers facing you. Quickly move the accelerometer to one side. Observe the angle of the string measured by the protractor. In what direction does the string move? What can you infer about the direction of acceleration? Try moving the accelerometer to the other side. What does this tell you?

5. Use the conversion chart to convert the angle reading on the accelerometer to an acceleration in meters per second per second.

6. Hold the accelerometer level and begin to run. Have a friend run with you and read the angle. Enter this data in the table.

DATA AND OBSERVATIONS

Sample Data

Moving Object	Acceleration m/s/s
75°	2.63
50°	8.22

Investigate 12-2 (continued)

ANALYZING

1. In what direction does the string move in comparison with the direction you move when you speed up? Describe. **The string moves in the opposite direction, away from the direction of motion.**

2. How did the string behave as you slowed down? **The string moved toward the direction of motion.**

CONCLUDING AND APPLYING

3. Describe the position of the string while you were moving with constant velocity. **The string hangs straight down.**

4. **Going Further:** Predict whether or not loose objects in a car would tend to move in the same direction of the string, or in the opposite direction. **They would move in the same direction as the accelerometer string.**

13-1 Acceleration of Falling Objects

Lab Preview

1. How do you calculate the distance from one image to the next? __Subtract the position of__ __the second image from the first.__

2. How many images of the ball are there in this activity? __six__

Two falling balls in Figure 13-2 on page 416 of your text were recorded by strobe photography. Ten photographs were taken each second, each 1/10 of a second apart. Even though the balls are of different masses, they are falling at the same rate. Figure 13-2 is a drawing made from that photograph. At one side of the figure is a two-meter measuring stick. As each ball falls, there seems to be more distance between each succeeding image. You learned in Chapter 12 that distance traveled in a given time is a measure of speed. Therefore, if the balls are moving greater distances in the same period of time, they are speeding up or accelerating. Use Figure 13-2 to discover the acceleration of these two falling objects.

PROBLEM
What is the acceleration of falling objects?

MATERIALS
ruler
data table
Figure 13-2

WHAT TO DO
1. Copy the data table *into your Journal.*
2. Using the ruler as a guide, record the position of the first image of one ball as it starts to fall. Always *measure* the ball position from the same point on the ball.
3. Record the position of the second image.
4. *Calculate* the distance from the first to the second image by subtracting the position of the first image from the position of the second image. Record this distance in the table under Image 2.
5. The images were taken 1/10 of a second apart. Use this information to *calculate* the average velocity of the balls between the first and second image in meter per second by dividing the distance fallen (in meters) by 1/10 second.
6. Record the position of the rest of the images. Make sure you always measure to the same place on the ball.
7. Find the distance between each pair of images and the average velocity. Fill these in for the rest of the images.
8. The last column of the table shows the exact time the balls' velocity reached the average velocity. To calculate these times, we assumed the clock started at the time of the first image and that the ball reached average velocity halfway in time between any two images.

Investigate 13-1 (continued)

Sample Data

DATA AND OBSERVATIONS

Image	Position (cm)	Distance Fallen (cm)	Average Velocity (m/s)	Time (S)
1	0			
2	10	5	0.5	0.10
3	20	15	1.5	0.20
4	44	24	2.4	0.30
5	78	34	3.4	0.40
6	123	45	4.5	0.50

ANALYZING

1. Did the velocity of the balls change as they fell? How do you know? __Yes; the average__ __velocity increased from Image 2 to 6. There was more space between images.__

2. Make a bar graph of your data. *Infer* what the bar graph tells about the position of the balls as they fall. __The distance the balls fell was greater during each time interval, therefore__ __their positions were further and further from the start after each time interval.__

CONCLUDING AND APPLYING

3. How much did the average velocity increase between the second and third images? Between the third and fourth images? __1.0 m/s between the second and third and 0.9 m/s between the__ __third and fourth images__

4. Going Further: *Calculate* the balls' acceleration. Find the acceleration between the image at 0.10 s and the image at 0.30 s by dividing the increase in velocity by the time interval in seconds. What was your result? __As measured in the sample data: The velocity increased 1.9 m/s__ __between 0.10 and 0.30. The acceleration was $\dfrac{1.9 \text{ m/s}}{0.2 \text{ s}} = 9.5 \text{ m/s}^2$__

13-2 The Period of a Pendulum

Lab Preview

1. What will you use to make a pendulum? **the string and one washer**

2. What string lengths will you be using? **Lengths will vary.**

A classic example of periodic motion is a pendulum in a grandfather clock. How does a pendulum help a clock keep time? What variables affect a pendulum's motion?

PROBLEM
What affects the period of a pendulum?

FORM A HYPOTHESIS
Think about the length of the pendulum, the bob mass, and amplitude (pull-back distance) of the pendulum. How do you think changing these variables will affect the period of the pendulum?

OBJECTIVES
- Separate and control variables in an experiment.
- Predict the effect of different tests on the period of a pendulum.

MATERIALS
ruler
string
masking tape
meterstick
metal washers
seconds timer

PLAN THE EXPERIMENT

1. Using the photo as a guide, explain how you will make your pendulum.
2. How will you measure the different variables?
3. Decide how you will vary each trial. The sample data tables will help guide you in your testing. Be sure you change only one variable in each trial.

CHECK THE PLAN

1. Prepare data tables in your Science Journal that are specific to your tests.
2. Have your teacher check your plan before you begin your experiment.

DATA AND OBSERVATIONS

Sample Data

Trial A

	Length = __50__ cm	Mass __2__ washers
Pullback Distance (cm)	Time for 10 Swings (s)	Pendulum Period (s)
10	14	1.4
20	14	1.4
30	14	1.4

Design Your Own Investigation 13-2 (continued)

Trial B

	Amplitude = __10__ cm	Length = __50__ cm
Pendulum Bob Weight (Number of Washers)	Time for 10 Swings (s)	Pendulum Period (s)
1	14	1.4
2	14	1.4
4	14	1.4

Trial C

	Amplitude = __20__ cm	Mass __2__ washers
Pendulum Length	Time for 10 Swings (s)	Pendulum Period (s)
30 cm	11	1.1
40 cm	12	1.2
60 cm	15	1.5

ANALYZE AND CONCLUDE

1. **Compare** Summarize the results of your experiment and compare them with your hypothesis. **Answers will vary.**

2. **Explain** Looking back at your comparison in the last question, explain the effect of changing the pendulum's bob mass, amplitude, and length on the pendulum period. **Changing length affected the period; neither changing mass nor amplitude had an effect.**

3. **Use Numbers** Draw a graph plotting the pendulum's period for the different string length. Using your graph, predict the pendulum's period for a string of 100 cm. What is the relationship between the change in length of string and the change in period? **Answers will vary depending on graphs, but should be about 2.0 s; the amount of increase will vary.**

GOING FURTHER
If you were building a pendulum clock, how would you build it to make sure the clock would be as accurate as possible? **Answers will vary but should include the idea that the length of the pendulum affects its period.**

Text Page 452   Chapter 14

14-1 Differences in Streams

Lab Preview

1. How do you adjust the supply of water in this activity? __by using the screw clamp on the__
   __supply hose__

2. What will you do to the sand in the stream table before trying each plan you develop?
   __smooth out the sloping sand from the previous channel__

You've seen how streams form, but do streams have different characteristics? During this Investigate you will make your own model of streams.

PROBLEM

What factors do you think control stream characteristics? Think about what you know about streams. How would you make your own streams? How can you control the flow?

MATERIALS

2 pails
plastic hose
2 screw clamps
stream table
sand
blocks of wood

SAFETY PRECAUTIONS

Wear an apron to protect your clothing.

WHAT TO DO

Work with your group and plan ways to set up your stream table to form different streams. Show your plan to your teacher. If you are advised to revise your plan, be sure to check with your teacher again before you begin. Carry out your plan keeping in mind:

1. When you set up the stream table, dampen the sand.
2. By using a screw clamp on the supply hose, you can adjust the flow of water.
3. Do not make the reservoir end higher than the other end of the stream table.
4. Smooth out the sloping sand from the previous channel before forming another one.

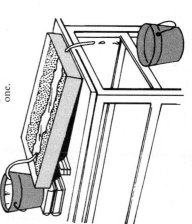

Investigate 14-1 (continued)

ANALYZING

1. How could the flow of water be increased? __by loosening the screw clamp__

2. How could the flow of water from the supply pail be slowed down? __by tightening the screw__
   __clamp__

3. Describe the channel that was formed when the sand end was high. __narrow and swift__

4. Describe the channel that was formed when the sand end was lower. __broad and slow__

CONCLUDING AND APPLYING

5. *Compare and contrast* the two types of stream channels. __The channel formed when the__
   __sand end was high was narrower and swifter than the channel formed when the sand end__
   __was lower.__

6. *Determine the cause* of the differences between the two channels you made. __The difference__
   __is caused by the change in slope.__

7. *Going Further:* What kind of stream channels would you expect to form on plains? What kind
   form in mountainous areas? __Broad channels form on plains. Narrow channels form in__
   __mountainous areas.__

DESIGN YOUR OWN INVESTIGATION

14-2 Ground Permeability

Lab Preview

1. How many soil samples will you be testing? __four__

2. Why do you need a watch with a second hand in this activity? __to determine the time it takes for the water to sink into the soil__

There are many different kinds of soils. Soils that have a lot of connecting pores are characterized as permeable. Permeability affects how fast water can seep into the soil and flows through the ground.

PROBLEM

What factors determine how fast water seeps into different soils?

FORM A HYPOTHESIS

As a group, discuss what factors might influence the permeability of different soils. Agree upon these factors, then make a hypothesis that can be tested in your investigation.

OBJECTIVES

- Predict and compare the permeability of different soils.
- Measure the time it takes for water to seep into different soils.

- Infer why some soils are more permeable than others.

MATERIALS

watch with second hand
25-mL graduated cylinder
600-mL beakers (4)
water
metric ruler
permanent markers
potting soil, clay, sand, gravel

PLAN THE EXPERIMENT

1. Examine the materials provided by your teacher. Decide which materials you will use and how you will use them in your experiment.

2. Design a procedure to test your hypothesis. Write down what you will do at each step of your test.

3. Design a table for recording data.

DATA AND OBSERVATIONS

Sample Data

Soil Combinations	Observations of Soil	Prediction	Amount of Time to Sink In
soil, sand	brown, gritty	permeable	1 min. 30 sec.

Design Your Own Investigation 14-2 (continued)

CHECK THE PLAN

1. Review how you will combine the different materials to create "test soils." Will your combinations create different-colored and -textured test soils?

2. Have you determined how you will measure the water as it seeps into the soil?

3. Before you start the experiment, have your teacher approve your plan.

4. Carry out your experiment. Complete your data table in your Science Journal or on a computer shreadsheet.

ANALYZE AND CONCLUDE

1. **Measure** Measure the time it takes for the water in the beaker to permeate the soil. Compare your observations with your hypothesis and your predictions, and record these in your data table. __Observations will vary.__

2. **Interpret Data** Which of the soils was least permeable? Most permeable? Water soaked fastest into this soil. The beaker containing gravel was the most permeable. Water took the longest time to soak into this soil. The beaker containing clay was the least permeable.

3. **Infer** Infer why some soils are more permeable than others. __Less permeable soils may have smaller pores or they might be more compacted. More permeable soils may have larger pore spaces and be less compacted.__

GOING FURTHER

Explain how permeability affects groundwater flow. Be sure to discuss runoff in your answer. __Water that falls on Earth's surface can become groundwater quicker in some places, depending on the permeability of the ground. Water soaks quickly into permeable soils, thus reducing the amount of runoff.__

DESIGN YOUR OWN INVESTIGATION

15-1 Stream Erosion and Deposition

Lab Preview

1. How many trials will you run in this activity? **more than one**

2. In this activity, how will you use the block of wood? **use it to carve a channel in the sand**

Streams are very effective movers of sediment. They can erode large quantities of sediment from an area and deposit them many miles away. But how do streams erode and deposit sediment, and where in the stream channel do these two processes take place?

PROBLEM

Which factors affect the way a stream erodes and deposits sediments?

FORM A HYPOTHESIS

As a group, list the factors that might influence stream erosion and deposition. Agree upon these factors, then form a hypothesis that can be tested in your experiment.

OBJECTIVES

- Design an experiment that tests the effects of different factors on stream erosion and deposition.
- Compare how different factors affect the way a stream erodes and deposits sediment.
- Determine where erosion and deposition occur in the stream channel.

MATERIALS

stream table
sand, small pebbles, soil
plastic hose
screw clamps
pails with water
block of wood

SAFETY

PLAN THE EXPERIMENT

1. Examine the materials provided by your teacher. Determine how you will use these materials to create a stream channel.

2. Agree upon a way to test your hypothesis. Write down what you will do at each step.

3. Design a table for recording your data.

DATA AND OBSERVATIONS

Answers will depend on the data tables developed by the students.

Design Your Own Investigation 15-1 (continued)

3. Before you start the experiment, have your teacher approve your plan.

4. Carry out your experiment. Complete your data table in your Science Journal.

CHECK THE PLAN

1. How many factors will you test to observe stream erosion and deposition? Keep in mind that you should only test one factor or variable at a time.

2. If you are testing more than one variable, how will you ensure that the same conditions exist in the stream channel for each test?

ANALYZE AND CONCLUDE

1. **Observe** Describe what happened to the stream channel in your tests. Where did most erosion take place? Where did deposition occur? **Answers will vary but may include that an increase in either slope of the channel or volume of water increased the amount of sediment that was eroded and deposited. Most erosion took place along the sides of the stream channel. Deposition occurred at the end of the stream channel.**

2. **Conclude** What happened to the eroded materials? Describe how they were deposited. **The eroded materials were deposited at different points along the stream bed. Larger sediments were deposited close to the top of the stream; smaller sediments were carried further by the moving water.**

3. **Compare and Contrast** Compare the effects of different factors on stream erosion and deposition. **Increasing either the slope of the channel or the volume of water increases the rate and amount of erosion. Because more sediments are eroded, more are deposited when the stream empties into a standing body of water.**

4. Explain how your results support or do not support your hypothesis. **Answers will vary but may include that an increase in slope of the channel increased erosion. Other factors may include water volume, shape of channel, and type of sediment.**

GOING FURTHER

Based on your observations, infer where the greatest amount of sediment might be found along a river's course. **The greatest amount of sediment would be found near the point where the river empties into the sea.**

15-2 How Do Glaciers Change the Land?

Lab Preview

1. What shape river channel will you be making in this activity? __V-shaped__

2. What electrical equipment will you need to use carefully? __lamp with reflector__

Glaciers erode the land and can change it a great deal. In this activity, you'll observe how glaciers change the land as they erode Earth's surface.

PROBLEM

How do valley glaciers affect Earth's surface?

MATERIALS

ice block about 5 cm by 20 cm by 2 cm, containing sand, clay, and gravel
stream table with sand
lamp with reflector
metric ruler

SAFETY PRECAUTIONS

You will be using electrical equipment near water in this Investigate. Please keep these items apart from one another.

WHAT TO DO

1. Copy the data table *into your Journal*. Then set up the stream table and lamp as shown in the photo on page 488 of your text.

2. The ice block is made by mixing water with sand, gravel, and clay in a container and then freezing (see photo *A*, page 489 of your text).

3. Make a V-shaped river channel. Measure and record its width and depth. Draw a sketch that includes these measurements (see photo *B*, page 489 of your text).

4. Place the ice block, to act as a moving glacier, at the upper end of the stream table.

5. Gently push the glacier along the river channel until it's under the light, halfway between the top and bottom of the stream table.

6. Turn on the light and allow the ice to melt. *Observe* and record what happens.

7. *Measure* and record the width and depth of the glacial channel. Draw a sketch of the channel and include these measurements *in your Journal*.

DATA AND OBSERVATIONS

Sample Data

	Width	Depth	Observation
River	3 cm	2 cm	V shaped
Glacier	5 cm	4 cm	U shaped

Investigate 15-2 (continued)

ANALYZING

1. How can you *infer* the direction from which a glacier traveled? __The area over which the glacier has moved will probably be smoother and have steeper sides than the section which has not eroded.__

2. How can you tell how far down the valley the glacier traveled? __The channel will be U-shaped to the point where the glacier stopped, and V-shaped past that point. Small deposits will form at the end of the glacier.__

CONCLUDING AND APPLYING

3. Determine the effect valley glaciers have on the surface over which they move. __Valley glaciers erode the surface like a bulldozer, leaving U-shaped valleys with steep sides and flat bottoms.__

4. Going Further: How can you identify land that was once covered by a glacier? __Glaciers leave behind characteristic deposits and patterns of erosion.__

DESIGN YOUR OWN INVESTIGATION

16-1 Succession

Lab Preview

1. What do you put in the jar? __distilled water and dried pond vegetation__

2. How many times will you take samples from the jar? __at least once a day__

How does a newly dug pond differ from one that has existed for years? In this investigation, you'll simulate a pond-water ecosystem to explore succession and to discover how new ponds fill with a variety of organisms.

PROBLEM

How does a pond-water ecosystem change?

FORM A HYPOTHESIS

As a group, write out a statement that predicts what will happen to the populations of organisms in a new pond-water ecosystem. Include in your hypothesis changes you might expect in color, smell, and other characteristics of the water.

OBJECTIVES

- Predict what happens in the succession of a pond-water ecosystem.
- Observe and explain changes in the ecosystem.

MATERIALS

large, clean jar and lid
dried pond vegetation or pond water
distilled water
eyedroppers
microscope, slides, and coverslips

SAFETY PRECAUTIONS

Wash your hands after handling the materials in this investigation.

PLAN THE EXPERIMENT

1. Examine the materials provided. Decide how to use them to make a pond-water ecosystem.

2. How long will you conduct your investigation? How will you make observations? How often will you make observations?

3. What will you be observing? Some things to observe are water color, cloudiness, odor, sediment, and other factors that may change. Microscopically, look for organisms seen below. Record how the number of organisms increases or decreases.

4. Design a data table in your Science Journal.

CHECK THE PLAN

1. How will you know when one organism increases and another decreases?

2. Make sure you have a variable and a control.

3. Make sure your teacher approves your plan before you proceed.

4. Carry out the investigation. Record your observations.

 Hydra

 Euglena

Paramecium

 Rotifer

 Spirogyra

 Volvox

 Anabaena

Daphnia

Design Your Own Investigation 16-1 (continued)

DATA AND OBSERVATIONS

Day	Notes	Sketches
1	Observations will vary, but should show increasing	
2	numbers and diversity of organisms.	
3		
4		

ANALYZE AND CONCLUDE

1. **Infer** What was the source of the organisms in the pond-water ecosystem? __pond vegetation__

2. **Observe** What changes occurred that were observable without a microscope? __Water darkened and became more opaque, smell became more vegetative, and more organisms appeared.__

3. **Observe** What changes occurred that were observable with a microscope? __Organisms of various kinds increased in number.__

4. **Observe** How many different organisms did you observe the first day? The last day? __There were more organisms on the last day than there were on the first.__

5. **Compare and Contrast** Did any of the organisms increase in number? Decrease? Explain how this may have occurred by making a general statement about succession that explains what happened in your pond ecosystem. __Algae and Euglena should have increased at the beginning. They are food producers. Then their numbers should have decreased at least relative to increases in other populations. Food producers increase in the beginning of pond life. Then food consumers, such as Hydra and Rotifers, increase as they consume the food producers.__

GOING FURTHER

Work in small groups to produce rough graphs that reflect the relative changes in the populations of organisms that you observed. What kind of graph would be best to use? __Graphs will differ but a horizontal bar graph would work well to represent increases in population over time.__

16-2 Getting Up-Close and Personal

Lab Preview

1. How many organisms will you identify in the ecosystem?   **at least two**

2. What will you use to study the organisms?   **a hand lens and/or binoculars**

Could you survive on a deserted island? Not without food! To get food you'd have to interact with other organisms in the ecosystem. In this activity, you'll find out more about how organisms in an ecosystem interact with one another.

PROBLEM

How do certain organisms interact in an ecosystem?

MATERIALS

Journal
hand lens or binoculars

WHAT TO DO

1. Choose an ecosystem near your school or home. It might be in a cluster of trees, a rotting log, a pond, a patch of weeds, or another setting.

2. Identify at least two organisms that are interacting within this ecosystem. You can include organisms that are not always present, but leave evidence of their interaction through tracks or feathers.

3. In the space below and *in your Journal*, create a table to record and date your observations.

4. Over the next week, plan as many observations as possible. Schedule them for different times of the day.

5. Use a hand lens and/or binoculars to study the organisms you chose. Be sure to record *in your Journal* how these organisms interact with each other and with the environment.

DATA AND OBSERVATIONS

Answers will vary depending on the ecosystems students' choose to observe.

Investigate 16-2 (continued)

ANALYZING   1.– 4. Answers will vary depending on ecosystems observed. Check for complete-ness of descriptions and logic of answers.

1. Describes the environment of your ecosystem.

2. **Spreadsheet** List all the populations of organisms present in the ecosystem. Put these data on your spreadsheet.

3. Which organisms did you study? Are they producers, consumers, or decomposers?

4. What evidence did you find of competition within the ecosystem? Cooperation? Interaction between organisms and their environment?

CONCLUDING AND APPLYING

5. What did each organism you studied do that helped it survive?   **Students should point out how consumers got food and shelter and how producers got sunlight and water.**

6. What might happen if one or both of the organisms you studied disappeared from this ecosystem?   **Students should realize that the loss of one** In what ways would the ecosystem be affected?   **or the other organism would result in upsetting other parts of the ecosystem.**

7. **Going Further:** Think of a change you could make in this ecosystem that would not deliberately damage it. *Predict* how the two organisms you studied would react to the change you suggest.   **Students should point out**
Then, test your prediction.   **Answers will vary depending on the ecosystem chosen. Be certain students' actions are not deliberately or inadvertently destructive. Students may realize that some actions taken (watering a lawn or garden) can actually benefit an ecosystem.**

INVESTIGATION
DESIGN YOUR OWN

17-1 Waves on a Coiled Spring

Lab Preview

1. Wearing safety goggles in this activity will protect your eyes from what? _the coiled spring_

2. What will you do with the yarn in this activity? _tie it to a coil near the middle of the spring_

You have learned about longitudinal and transverse waves. How do waves travel on a coiled spring? Are they transverse waves or longitudinal waves?

PROBLEM

How many types of waves can you create with a coiled spring?

FORM A HYPOTHESIS

As a group, decide on a hypothesis that predicts how waves can travel on a coiled spring. Write it down.

SAFETY PRECAUTIONS

OBJECTIVES

• Observe how waves travel along a coiled spring.
• Operationally define types of waves.

MATERIALS

coiled metal spring
piece of colored yarn

PLAN THE EXPERIMENT

1. Examine the materials and decide how you will test your hypothesis. Write down your plan.

2. In your Science Journal, prepare a place to draw diagrams of the wave types your group creates with the coiled spring. Plan to use arrows on the diagrams to show direction of movement.

CHECK THE PLAN

1. Determine if two people will hold the spring or you will let the spring hang down.

2. Before you begin, check your plan with your teacher.

3. Do the experiment. Make certain that you observe closely to see what kinds of waves you can make and to see what happens to the waves when they reach the end of the coil. Do they come back? Observe closely and in your Science Journal draw diagrams of what occurs.

Rarefaction

Compression

Design Your Own Investigation 17-1 (continued)

ANALYZE AND CONCLUDE

1. **Observe** What types of wave pulses did you create? _transverse and longitudinal_

2. **Interpret Data** Draw a diagram of each type of wave that occurred in the spring. Label your diagrams. Show direction of the movement. _Students should draw the diagrams in their Science Journals._

3. Did the waves move in the same direction as the source of the disturbance? Explain. _The transverse wave moved at a right angle to the source of the disturbance. The longitudinal wave traveled in the same direction as the disturbance._

4. **Observe** What happened when the waves reached the end of the spring? _The wave came back along the spring. A transverse wave remained transverse and a longitudinal wave remained a longitudinal wave._

5. **Infer** Compare the motion of a radio speaker tested in the Find Out! activity to the waves you created with the spring. Is a sound wave a transverse or longitudinal wave? Is an ocean wave a transverse or longitudinal wave? _longitudinal, transverse_

GOING FURTHER

Observe how fast transverse and longitudinal waves move along the spring. Can you change the speed or is there a set speed? _Use a stopwatch to measure the waves. There is a set speed._

I N V E S T I G A T E !

17-2 Ripples

Text Page 552 — Chapter **17**

Lab Preview

1. How will you create waves in the water? **by using a pencil or pen to tap the surface of the water**

2. How do you shorten the wavelength in this activity? **by tapping the water faster and increasing the frequency**

Do water waves behave the same as people waves and spring waves? How are their speed, frequency, and wavelength related? In this activity you will use the patterns produced by light shining through the crests and troughs of waves in a shallow dish to investigate water waves.

PROBLEM

How are a wave's frequency and wavelength related?

MATERIALS

clear glass dish approximately 30-cm square
pencil or pen
1 piece of blank white paper
strips of plastic foam
tape
water
overhead light
ruler

SAFETY PRECAUTIONS

WHAT TO DO

1. Tape strips of plastic foam to the inner edges of the dish (see photo **A**, page 553 of your text). Then, fill the clear glass dish with about 3 cm of water (see photo **B**, page 553 of your text). Set it on a piece of blank white paper under an overhead light source.

2. Tap the water with the end of your pencil or pen. Observe the wave by looking at the paper. In the space provide below or *in your Journal*, draw the shape of the wave. Compare the speed of the wave in all directions. How fast does the wave travel? Estimate how long it takes to travel the length of the dish.

3. Now, tap the water again, producing a series of waves. Increase the frequency by tapping the water faster and observe the change in wavelength. Draw an example of low- and high-frequency waves being produced.

DATA AND OBSERVATIONS

Responses will vary depending on students' observations.

Investigate 17-2 (continued)

ANALYZING

1. What effect does increasing the frequency have on the wavelength of the waves produced in Step 3? **Increasing the frequency causes the wavelength to decrease.**

2. What would happen to the wavelength if you decreased the frequency? **The wavelength would increase.**

CONCLUDING AND APPLYING

3. What is the relationship between wavelength and frequency in water waves? **Wavelength and frequency are inversely proportional (as one increases, the other decreases).**

4. **Going Further:** Predict whether the wave speed depends on the water depth. *In your Journal* write a plan about how you could make different depths of water in the same dish and find out. **Wave speed is related to water depth. Changing the depth has the same effect as changing the medium. Water waves generally travel faster in shallower water than in deeper waters. Students' plans might include using various thicknesses of foam to simulate a basin with different depths or slightly elevating one edge of the dish.**

73

74

DESIGN YOUR OWN INVESTIGATION

18-1 Locating Active Volcanoes

Lab Preview

1. How will you use the tracing paper? **to trace Earth's surface**

2. What will you add to the tracing to help with location? **lines of latitude and longitude, locations of 20 active volcanoes**

Volcanoes form when hot, melted rock material is forced upward to Earth's surface. As the melted rock moves inside Earth, vibrations occur, which are felt as earthquakes. How would you determine whether active volcanoes are located near earthquake epicenters?

PROBLEM

Is there a connection between the locations of active volcanoes and the locations of recent earthquakes?

FORM A HYPOTHESIS

As a group, discuss the areas where earthquakes and volcanoes are commonly located. Then form a hypothesis about whether you expect to see a relationship between the locations of active volcanoes and the locations of earthquake epicenters.

OBJECTIVES

- Plot the locations of several active volcanoes.
- Describe patterns of distribution for volcanoes and earthquake epicenters.
- Relate the locations of active volcanoes to the locations of recent earthquakes.

MATERIALS

world map (Appendix H)
tracing paper

Volcano	Latitude	Longitude
#1	64°N	19°W
#2	28°N	34°E
#3	43°S	172°E
#4	35°N	136°E
#5	18°S	68°W
#6	25°S	114°W
#7	20°N	155°W
#8	54°N	167°W
#9	16°N	122°E
#10	28°N	17°W

Volcano	Latitude	Longitude
#11	15°N	43°E
#12	6°N	75°W
#13	64°S	158°E
#14	38°S	78°E
#15	21°S	56°E
#16	38°N	26°E
#17	7°S	13°W
#18	2°S	102°E
#19	38°N	30°W
#20	54°N	159°E

Design Your Own Investigation 18-1 (continued)

PLAN THE EXPERIMENT

1. As a group, agree upon a way to test your hypothesis. Write down what you will do at each step of your test.
2. Examine the volcano latitude and longitude chart. What is the best way to plot the data on a tracing of Earth's surface?
3. Examine the map of earthquake epicenters on page 578. How will you compare your data with this map?

CHECK THE PLAN

Discuss and decide upon the following points and write them down.

1. As a group, decide how you will summarize your data.
2. How will you determine whether certain facts or conditions indicate a correlation between the locations of active volcanoes and earthquake epicenters?
3. Make sure your teacher approves your experiment before you proceed.
4. Carry our your experiment. Record your observations.

ANALYZE AND CONCLUDE

1. **Interpret Scientific Illustrations** Describe any patterns of distribution formed by active volcanoes. **Answers may vary. Most volcanoes occur along the Pacific Ring of Fire.**

2. **Interpret Scientific Illustrations** Describe any patterns of distribution formed by earthquake epicenters. **Answers may vary. Most earthquakes also occur along the Pacific Ring of Fire.**

3. **Compare and Contrast** How did the patterns that you observed in the distribution of volcanoes compare with the locations of earthquake epicenters? **The pattern of distribution of volcanoes and earthquakes is similar.**

GOING FURTHER

How are the locations of volcanoes and earthquake epicenters related to Earth's geographic features? **Students should see the relationship of active volcanoes and earthquake epicenters around the Pacific Ocean. They should notice that earthquakes and active volcanoes also occur in the vicinity of Earth's moving plate boundaries and hot spots.**

Accept all proposals for testing student hypotheses, and discuss those that sound reasonable as well as those that do not.

18-2 Making a Model Seismograph

Lab Preview

1. This activity requires two people. Describe what each person will do to record seismic vibrations. **One person will pull a sheet of paper under the marker while the other person will strike the table several times.**

2. What portion of a wave is defined as amplitude? **half the height of the wave from crest to trough**

In this activity, you will make a model seismograph and record some vibrations.

PROBLEM

How can you measure the magnitude of vibrations?

MATERIALS

ring stand with ring
wire hook from coat hanger
masking tape
sheet of paper
piece of string
2 rubber bands
fine-tip marker
metric ruler

WHAT TO DO

1. Copy the data table *into your Journal*.
2. Set up your seismograph using the illustration on page 591 of your text as a guide.

3. Place a sheet of paper under the ring. Adjust the position of the marker so that its tip just touches near the end of the paper.

4. Work with a partner. While one person strikes the table several times with equal strength, the other one should slowly pull the paper under the marker.

5. Recall from Chapter 17 that amplitude is half the height of wave from crest to trough. *Measure* the amplitude marked on your paper. Record your measurements and observations as Trial 1.

6. *Hypothesize* about the effect of the magnitude of the vibrations on the amplitude of the peaks.

7. Repeat Steps 3 and 4, hitting the table with less strength for Trial 2 and more strength for Trial 3. Record your measurements and observations.

DATA AND OBSERVATIONS

Sample Data

Trial Number	Amplitude (Height of Marks)	Observations
1	3 mm	Frame moves a little
2	1 mm	Frame doesn't seem to move
3	6 mm	Frame moves noticeably

Investigate 18-2 (continued)

ANALYZING

1. Which trial resulted in the greatest amplitudes recorded on the wavy line? **Trial 3**

2. How did the movement of the marker compare with the movement of the frame of the seismograph? **In a real seismograph, the pen would remain stationary while the frame moved with the vibrations. Students' models don't do this because the pen is not isolated from the motion of the frame.**

CONCLUDING AND APPLYING

3. How does your hypothesis *compare* with the results of the activity? **Responses will vary depending on students' hypotheses.**

4. Determine the effect the magnitude of vibrations had on the amplitude of the wave peaks. **As the magnitude of the vibrations increased, the amplitude of the wave peaks increased.**

5. Going Further: What difference would you *predict* between the amplitudes generated by a strong earthquake and those generated by a weaker one? **Strong earthquakes should generate greater amplitudes.**

DESIGN YOUR OWN INVESTIGATION

19-1 Tilt and Temperature

Lab Preview

1. Why should you handle lamps carefully in experiments? __Lamps produce heat and__ __could cause burns.__

2. What instrument will you use to determine the angle of the lamp light? __a protractor__

Earth's tilt causes the amount of sunlight that strikes Earth to vary from one hemisphere to the other, depending on the season. How might this affect the amount of heat from the sun received by an area?

PROBLEM

How is the angle at which light strikes an area related to the amount of heat energy received by that area?

FORM A HYPOTHESIS

As a group, discuss the effects of light striking an area from several different angles. At what angle would the area receive the most heat? Agree upon a hypothesis that can be tested in your experiment.

OBJECTIVES

- Use a model to measure the amount of heat received by an area from light striking the area at different angles.
- Describe how the angle at which light strikes an area is related to Earth's changing seasons.

POSSIBLE MATERIALS

black construction paper
protractor
Celsius thermometer
watch
tape
gooseneck lamp with 75-watt bulb

SAFETY

Do not touch the lamp. The lightbulb and shade can be hot even when the lamp has been turned off. Handle the thermometer carefully. If it breaks, do not touch anything. Inform your teacher immediately.

PLAN THE EXPERIMENT

1. As a group, agree upon how you will use the materials provided to test your hypothesis.
2. Write down exactly what you will do during each step of your test.
3. Make a list of any special properties you expect to observe or test.
4. Identify any constants, variables, and controls in your experiment.

DATA AND OBSERVATIONS

Sample Data

Temperature At	Start	3 Min.	6 Min.	9 Min.
Direct Light	27°	33°	34.5°	35°
Angled Light	27°	31°	32°	33°

Design Your Own Investigation 19-1 (continued)

CHECK THE PLAN

1. How will you determine whether the length of time the light is turned on affects heat energy?
2. How will you determine whether the angle at which light strikes an area causes changes in heat and energy?
3. Make sure your teacher approves your experiment before you proceed.
4. Carry out your experiment. Record your observations.

ANALYZE AND CONCLUDE

1. **Observe** Did the temperature in the envelope continue to rise at the same rate every three minutes? __no__

2. **Interpret Data** How does the angle of light affect temperature? How might this be related to Earth's changing seasons? __When light is angled, temperature increases more slowly.__ __When sunlight strikes Earth's surface at an angle, temperatures are lower than when__ __sunlight strikes Earth's surface from directly above. Thus, if a part of Earth is__ __experiencing winter, sunlight is not striking that part of Earth at a direct angle.__

3. **Design an Experiment** Did your experiment support your hypothesis? If not, determine how you might change the experiment in order to retest your hypothesis. __Answers will vary__ __depending on students' hypotheses.__

GOING FURTHER

Predict how the absorption of heat would be affected by changing your independent variables. Try your experiment with different values for your independent variables. __Students should realize__ __that lowering the angle should cause less of a temperature rise, and increasing the angle to__ __a greater amount should cause the temperature to rise more quickly.__

19-2 Eclipses and Moon Phases

Lab Preview

1. In this activity, what object represents the sun?   the unshaded light source

2. Why are you cautioned to observe thermal safety in this exercise?   because the light source grows hot very quickly and may cause burns if touched

You know that moon phases and solar eclipses result from the relative positions of the sun, the moon, and Earth. In this activity, you will demonstrate the positions of these bodies during certain phases and eclipses. You will also see why only a very small portion of Earth sees a total solar eclipse.

PROBLEM

How can you demonstrate moon phases and solar eclipses?

MATERIALS

pencil
unshaded light source
polystyrene ball
globe

SAFETY PRECAUTIONS

Be careful, the exposed bulb will be hot.

WHAT TO DO

1. Copy the data table *into your Journal.*
2. Stick the pencil into the polystyrene ball, *making a model* moon with a handle.

3. Set the globe and the lamp on the table about 0.5 m apart and turn on the light.

4. Holding the model moon by its pencil handle, move it around the globe to duplicate the position that will cause a solar eclipse. Record your observations in the data table and *in your Journal.*

5. Use this sun-Earth-moon model to duplicate the phases of the moon. During which phase(s) of the moon could a solar eclipse occur? How can you use the model to observe the umbra and penumbra of the moon?

DATA AND OBSERVATIONS

Sample Data

Moon Phase	Observations
New	Solar eclipse
First Quarter	No eclipse
Full	No eclipse
Third Quarter	No eclipse

Investigate 19-2 (continued)

ANALYZING

1. During which phase(s) of the moon is it possible for a solar eclipse to occur?   new moon phase

2. *Determine the effect* that a small change in the distance between Earth and the moon would have on the size of the shadow during an eclipse.   The smaller the distance between Earth and the moon, the larger the shadow.

3. As seen from Earth, how does the apparent size of the moon *compare* with the apparent size of the sun? How can an eclipse be used to confirm this?   The apparent size of the moon is the same as the apparent size of the sun. This can be demonstrated during a solar eclipse because the moon appears to completely cover the sun.

CONCLUDING AND APPLYING

4. Why doesn't a solar eclipse occur every month? Explain your answer.   because the orbit of the moon is not in the same plane as Earth's orbit around the sun

5. Suppose you wanted to make a more accurate model of the movement of the moon around Earth. How might you adjust the distance between the light source and the globe you are using? How would you adjust the size of the moon model in comparison with the globe you are using?   Move the light source farther away. Use a smaller ball.

6. *Going Further: Hypothesize* what would happen if the sun, the moon, and Earth were lined up with Earth directly in between the sun and moon.   Earth would cast a shadow on the moon.